Lightning in Harness

FOUNDATIONS OF SCIENCE LIBRARY

The Natural World
(4 volumes)

The Majesty of the Heavens
(Foundations of Astronomy)

The Round World
(Foundations of Geology and Geomorphology)

The Skies and the Seas
(Foundations of Meteorology, Oceanography & Cartography)

The Ages of the Earth
(Foundations of Palaeogeography and Palaeontology)

The Biological Sciences
(6 volumes)

The Life of Animals without Backbones
(Foundations of Invertebrate Zoology)

The Life of Animals with Backbones
(Foundations of Vertebrate Zoology)

The World of Plants
(Foundations of Botany)

Breeding and Growing
(Foundations of Genetics, Anthropology and Agriculture)

Patterns of Living
(Foundations of Ecology)

Human Kind
(Foundations of Human Biology)

The Physical Sciences
(9 volumes)

The Restlessness of Matter
(Foundations of Aerodynamics, Hydrodynamics and Thermodynamics)

The Science of Movement
(Foundations of Mechanics and Sound)

Lightning in Harness
(Foundations of Electricity)

The Silent Energy
(Foundations of Electrical Technology)

The Cathode Ray Revolution
(Foundations of Electronics)

The Rays of Light
(Foundations of Optics)

The Unseen Spectrum
(Foundations of Electromagnetic Radiation)

The Cosmic Power
(Foundations of Nuclear Physics)

The Discipline of Numbers
(Foundations of Mathematics)

The Chemical Sciences
(4 volumes)

The Fundamental Materials
(Foundations of Basic Chemistry)

The Elements and their Order
(Foundations of Inorganic Chemistry)

The Giant Molecules
(Foundations of Organic Chemistry)

The Chemist at Work
(Foundations of Analysis and Laboratory Techniques)

Technology
(5 volumes)

The Metallic Skills
(Foundations of Metallurgy)

Industrial Processing
(Foundations of Industrial and Chemical Technology)

Engineering Technology
(Foundations of Applied Engineering)

Automobile Engineering
(Foundations of Car Mechanics)

The Inventive Genius
(Foundations of Scientific Inventions)

History and Reference
(3 volumes)

The Beginnings of Science
(Foundations of Scientific History)

Frontiers of Science
(Foundations of Research Methods)

A Dictionary of Scientific Terms
(The Foundations of Science Reference Book)

CHIEF EDITORS

Leslie Basford, B.Sc.   Philip Kogan, M.Sc.

ASSISTANT EDITORS

Michael Dempsey, B.A., Michael Gabb, B.Sc., Clare Dover, B.Sc.
Cyril Parsons, B.Sc., Joan Pick, B.Sc., Michael Chinery, B.A.
David Larkin, B.Sc., Paul Drury Byrne, B.Sc.

CONSULTANT EDITORIAL BOARD

Sir Lawrence Bragg, M.C., O.B.E., F.R.S., M.A., Nobel Laureate
Sir James Chadwick, F.R.S., Ph.D., M.Sc., Nobel Laureate
Norman Fisher, M.A.
Sir Harry Melville, K.C.B., F.R.S., Ph.D., D.Sc.
Professor J. Z. Young, F.R.S., M.A.

Lightning in Harness

Foundations of Electricity

LESLIE BASFORD B.Sc. JOAN PICK B.Sc.

FOUNDATIONS OF SCIENCE LIBRARY

THE PHYSICAL SCIENCES

DISTRIBUTED IN THE U.S.A. BY
Ginn and Company : *BOSTON*
PUBLISHED BY
Sampson Low, Marston and Co : *LONDON*

This new presentation assembles
freshly edited material from
'Understanding Science' on one
subject into a single volume.

Library of Congress Catalog Card
Number: 66–17976

Catalog No.: L–20680

Made and printed in Great Britain by
Purnell & Sons Ltd., Paulton
(Somerset) and London

ELECTRICITY

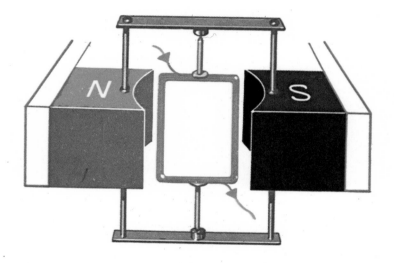

Contents

The Flow of an
Electric Current

An Electric Circuit

OF ALL the forms of energy, electricity is the most baffling and difficult to describe. A current cannot be seen. In fact it does not exist outside the wires and so on which carry it. A 'live' wire carrying a current looks exactly the same and weighs exactly the same as it does when it is not carrying a current.

An electric *current* is simply a movement or *flow* of electricity. The electricity is carried by minute particles called *electrons*. Electrons are very much smaller than atoms – in fact the outermost part of every atom consists of a number of electrons whirling around a central core or nucleus. Each electron has the same charge or 'packet' of electricity described as a *negative* charge. Usually the nucleus has exactly enough *positive* electrical charges to balance the negative charges on the electrons so that the atom as a whole is neutral.

A few of the electrons in each atom of a conductor such as copper are only loosely held. These 'free electrons' can jump from atom to atom and it is a steady drift of free electrons that carries electricity through a wire.

Why should electrons move about between atoms? The basic law of electricity says that two charges having the same sign (either both positive or both negative) repel each other; two charges having opposite signs (one positive and the other negative) attract each other. Since electrons carry negative charges they are repelled by negatively charged atoms and attracted by positively charged atoms.

As a result the electrons are pushed around from atom to atom until they find one with a shortage of electrons. Alternatively an electron may stay in an atom if it pushes another electron out. When some kind of 'driving force' is applied to the wire the wandering electrons are organised into a steady one-way drift. The driving force is simply a difference of electrical pressure (voltage) between the ends of the wire. It is provided by either a battery or generator (dynamo). Electrical pressure starts the drift of electrons by pushing the loosely held electrons from the first atom in the line to the next atom and so on.

Two points that must be borne in mind regarding the flow of electricity along a wire are, first, that the electrons which set out from one end are not the same electrons that reach the other end. Secondly, that by convention a current is said to flow through a circuit from the positive terminal of a battery to the negative terminal. In fact the moving electrons flow in the opposite direction. This confusing state of affairs dates back to early studies in electricity and cannot easily be put right now.

A current of electricity must have a completely unbroken path or circuit. If we could follow a current as it flowed along a wire we should eventually arrive back at our starting point. Wires which lead the current from one part of the circuit to another are nearly always made of copper. Copper, like most metals, is a good *conductor* of electricity; it has plenty of free electrons so a current has little difficulty in travelling through copper. Actually the best conductor is silver, but this metal would be far too expensive for wiring a house. Rubber and plastics are good insulators (or, what amounts to the same thing, bad conductors). An insulator is made up of atoms that do *not* have any loosely held electrons and these materials are used for covering electric wires so that if the out-going and returning parts of the wires touch there will not be any short cut for the current that reduces the planned length of the circuit (i.e., a 'short circuit'). There is a danger that a short circuit will cause a great unplanned rush of current through the circuit that causes overheating. This can cause a fire if the wires rest against wood or anything else that is inflammable.

The diagram shows we can trace a typical circuit around which current flows from a generator and back again to its starting point. The current starts out along cables supported on pylons. These cables are not insulated with rubber or plastic – they do not have to be because the large amount of air which surrounds them is an excellent insulator. Of course they are insulated from the pylon by glass blocks like that shown in the diagram, otherwise the electrons would short-cut through the pylon to the Earth. The current passes into insulated underground cables or overhead wires that bring it to the house.

As soon as it enters the house the current passes through the main fuses, then the circuit divides to lead the current to all the different lamps and power points. Each of the subsidiary circuits should have its own fuse. A fuse is a thin piece of wire made from a low-melting-point metal. When the current is more than the wiring can safely carry the fuse gets hot, because it is not such a good conductor as

An atom is neutral (uncharged) when the number of positively charged particles (protons) in its nucleus is equal to the number of negatively charged particles (electrons) outside the nucleus. If the atom as a whole gains extra electrons it becomes negatively charged, if it loses electrons it becomes positively charged.

A copper atom always has 29 protons ($+$). The copper atoms on the left are all negatively charged because they have more than 29 electrons ($-$). The copper atoms on the right are all positively charged because they have less than 29 electrons ($-$).

Electrons are repelled by negative atoms and attracted to positive atoms. That is why electrons flow along a wire, passing from atom to atom as shown in the diagram. But it is not always the incoming electron itself that passes on to the next atom, it may instead push out one of the loosely bound electrons already present.

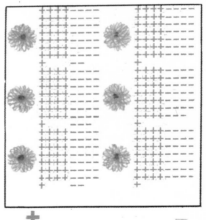

The picture shows, in a very much simplified manner, the circuit of an electric lamp. The wires in the house form only a small part of the complete circuit, for the wires which bring the current from the power station many miles away are also part of the same circuit.

Inset A shows one of the massive glass insulators that prevent the current passing into the pylons supporting the cables. The ridges are to throw off rain water that could otherwise form a conducting path over the insulator.

Inset B shows the main fuse. It is usually a thin wire made of some metal that melts easily when it is heated.

Inset C shows one of the smaller fuses that protects each of the subsidiary circuits branching off from the main fuse box. The fuse wires which are mounted on blocks of porcelain (a good insulator), are thick enough to carry a certain amount of current without getting hot. But an excessive current causes them to overheat, melt and break the circuit.

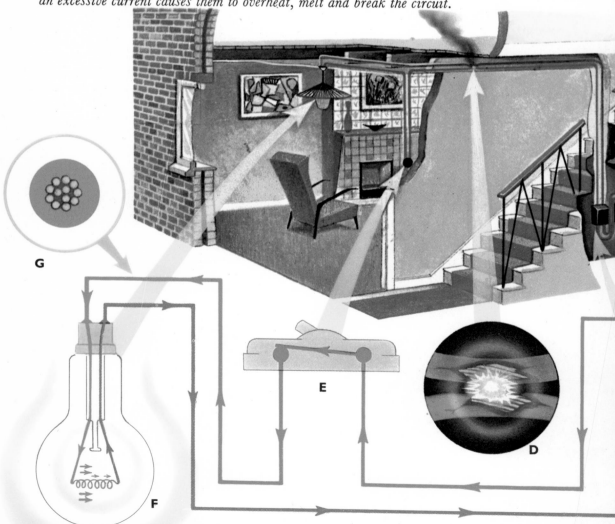

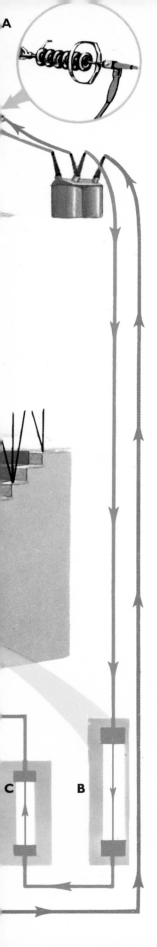

A

C   B

Inset D *shows a 'short circuit' caused by the insulation of two adjacent wires being damaged. Current passes directly from the supply wire to the return wire because this path is shorter than having to flow around the rest of the circuit. Sparks and a great deal of heat are produced as the current leaps across the slight gap between the wires.*

Inset E *shows a switch that can be opened to break the circuit and to stop the flow of current to the lamp.*

Inset F *shows an electric light bulb containing a coil of tungsten wire so fine that it is made white-hot by the current passing through it. The bulb is usually filled with argon, a gas that does not combine with tungsten.*

Inset G *shows a cross section through one of the wires used in this circuit. It is made up of several strands of copper twisted together, making it much more flexible than a single copper wire of the same diameter. Copper is a very good conductor of electricity; the rubber or plastic which covers the wire is a very good insulator.*

the rest of the circuit, and melts. So the circuit is broken and the current stops. In the diagram the subsidiary circuit leads current from the fuse box, by way of a switch, to a light bulb. If the switch were open no flow of electricity could take place in that particular circuit.

In the lamp is one of the few parts of the circuit that offers much resistance to the movement of electrons. This is the filament, a long coil of very fine tungsten wire. The electrons in tungsten are more tightly bound to atoms than they are in copper and consequently there is no easy drift of electrons through the filament. In fact the filament is made white-hot by the electrical energy expended in forcing electrons through it. Unlike a fuse the tungsten wire has a very high melting point and does not break, even at white heat.

Current emerging from the filament returns to the fuse box and completes its journey back to the generator through cables laid alongside the ones that carried it to the lamp.

The flashlight illustrated here is a familiar example of a circuit that has no wires. The current (by which we mean the conventional current from positive to negative), flows from the positive terminal of the battery. This is a central rod of carbon – one of the few non-metals that conducts electricity – fitted with a brass cap over its exposed end. Because of the chemical action going on in its battery the atoms in the carbon rod are unbalanced and have a shortage of electrons (i.e., positive charge). At the same time the atoms in the zinc casing of the battery have a surplus of electrons (i.e., negative charge). One end of the filament in

9

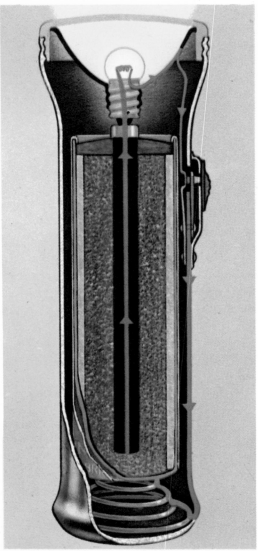

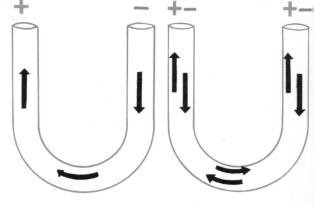

Chemical actions in the battery of this flashlight put a positive charge onto its central carbon rod and a negative charge onto its zinc shell. Electrons flow from the zinc through the metal of the torch and back by way of the bulb to the carbon rod. But the convention is to pretend that electric current flows from plus to minus, not in the direction the electrons really flow — from negative to positive. The arrows show the 'conventional' direction.

The diagram on the left shows a wire having a positive charge at one end and a negative charge at the other. The electrons flow in the same direction all the time. This is a direct current *(D.C.).*

The diagram on the right shows a wire where the charges at the ends are periodically switched round causing electrons to flow first one way and then the other. This to-and-from movement of electrons is an alternating current *(A.C.).*

the flashlight bulb is connected to a spot of solder on the bottom of the bulb end and this makes contact with the brass cap on the carbon rod. The other end of the filament is connected to the metal part of the base which screws into the reflector. Since the reflector is made of bare metal the current passes easily through it to a strip of brass leading to a switch on the side. As long as the switch is closed the current flows through it into the metal barrel of the flashlight itself. At the bottom of the flashlight barrel is a

spring which serves both to hold the batteries in place and also to provide a conducting path between the flashlight barrel and the zinc casing of the battery. The zinc casing forms the battery's negative terminal, its side insulated by a cardboard outer casing.

And so the current has completed its journey back to the battery. For simplicity the diagram shows only one cell whereas in practice the flashlight would contain a battery of two or more cells.

CHAPTER TWO

Ohm's Law

PROVIDING the physical conditions, such as the temperature, do not alter, the current (i.e. the rate of movement of *electrons*) flowing through a wire is directly proportional to the *potential difference* (i.e. the electrical 'pressure' difference which makes the electrons move) between the ends of the wire.

This statement is known as OHM'S LAW. As an example of Ohm's Law suppose that a current of 4 amps is flowing through an electric fire connected to the 240 volt mains supply. What would the current be if the mains voltage fell to 120 volts? Ohm's Law tells us that since the potential difference (voltage) has been halved, the current will be reduced in the same proportion, i.e. halved. The new current is therefore 2 amps. If the voltage had dropped to 80 volts (i.e. 1/3 of its original value) the current would drop proportionately to 4/3 amps (i.e. 1/3 of its original

value). In each case $\dfrac{\text{voltage}}{\text{current}}$ is the same: $\dfrac{240}{4} = 60, \dfrac{120}{2} = 60, \dfrac{80}{4/3} = 60$. Thus Ohm's Law can be stated in the form of an equation:

$$\frac{\text{voltage}}{\text{current}} = \text{a constant}$$

If the voltage, or potential difference, is measured in volts and the current

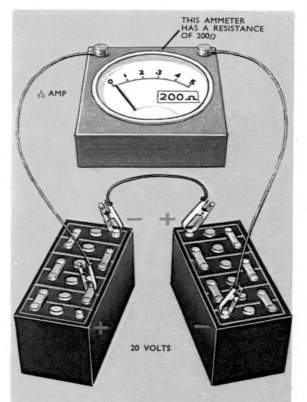

The total resistance (R) of the circuit is 200 ohms and the current (I) flowing is $\frac{1}{10}$ amp. Hence voltage (V) between terminals of meter is
V = I × R = $\frac{1}{10}$ amp × 200 ohms = 20 volts. The symbol for ohms is Ω.

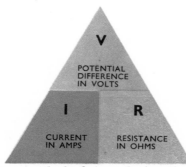

An easy method of remembering the Ohm's Law equations:—cover up the quantity to be found and the two remaining symbols give the required formula.

The *current* is the quantity of water which flows under the bridge in one second. An *electric current* is the quantity of electrons which flow in one second.

The movement of water is caused by a difference in height between the ends of the river. A movement of electrons is caused by a difference in potential between the ends of a wire. Potential difference is called voltage.

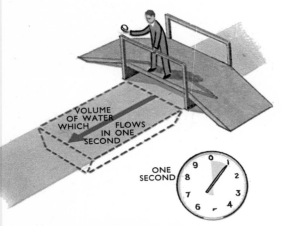

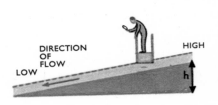

The greater the height difference the greater the flow of water. Similarly the greater the potential difference (voltage), the greater is the electric current. Doubling the height difference doubles the flow of water – doubling the potential difference (voltage) doubles the electric current. This is Ohm's Law.

The 'narrowness' of the river also controls the quantity of water which flows under the bridge in one second. If the river is very narrow, the current is small. Similarly the *resistance* of a wire controls the flow of electrons. If the resistance is very high, the electric current is small. If the resistance is low (equivalent to a wide river) the current is high.

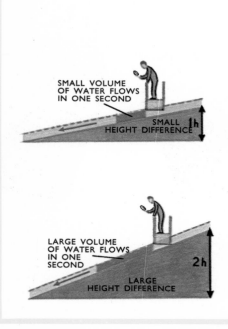

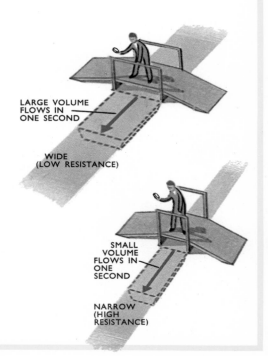

is measured in amps then the constant, instead of being just a number, is *by definition* a measure of the *resistance* of the wire, i.e. a measure of the wire's opposition to the flow of current through it. Resistance is measured in units called *ohms*.

Hence resistance (in ohms) =

$$\frac{\text{potential difference}}{\text{current}} = \frac{\text{volts}}{\text{amps}}.$$

Resistances measured in ohms are usually denoted by the symbol R, potential difference in volts is usually denoted by the symbol V and current in amps is usually denoted by the symbol I. Using these symbols Ohm's Law can be written as a kind of 'shorthand' equation: $R = \dfrac{V}{I}$.

Rearranging the equation gives $V = I \times R$ or $I = \dfrac{V}{R}$.

The resistance of the electric fire mentioned previously is obviously 60 ohms since $R = \dfrac{V}{I} = \dfrac{240 \text{ volts}}{4 \text{ amps}}$.

(Actually the resistance would be less when the fire was cold since the resistance of most metals increases with temperature. This is why Ohm's Law is true only if the physical conditions do not alter.) A resistance of 60 ohms presents a moderately high opposition to the passage of an electric current: if the fire had a low resistance of say 2 ohms, it would present a much easier path and much larger currents would flow through it. What current would flow through a fire having a resistance of 2 ohms if it were connected to the 240 volt mains supply? Because current, symbol I, is to be found the equation to use is the one which has I on the left-hand side. $I = \dfrac{V}{R}$. V = 240 volts, R = 2

ohms, hence $I = \dfrac{240}{2} = 120$ amps.

This is an enormous current and would 'blow' the fuses as soon as the fire was switched on. The greatest current that a household fuse will carry is usually 15 amps. What would be the resistance of an electric fire which just drew this amount of current from the 240 volt mains? Here resistance, symbol R, is to be found, so the best equation to use is the one which has R on the left-hand side. $R = \dfrac{V}{I}$. V = 240 volts, I = 15 amps, hence $R = \dfrac{240}{15} = 16$ ohms.

As well as making it possible to measure resistance (from the equation $R = \dfrac{V}{I}$) Ohm's Law provides an easy method of measuring voltage. A simple voltmeter is really a current-measuring instrument, or ammeter, showing current (I) amps which the voltage (V) being examined sends through a known resistance (R) ohms. The size of the voltage can be found from the equation $V = I \times R$. (This calculation does not have to be performed in practice because the calibrations of the voltmeter have already taken it into account.) Supposing a meter, whose total resistance is 200 ohms, registers a current of $\frac{1}{10}$ amp, what is the voltage driving the current through the meter? In other words, what is the potential difference between the terminals of the meter? From the equation

$$V = I \times R$$

(this is the best equation to use here since it is the one where V appears on the left) the voltage in question is plainly

$\frac{1}{10}$ amps $\times$ 200 ohms = 20 volts.

CHAPTER THREE

Resistances in Series and Parallel

THE current flowing in a circuit depends upon the voltage applied to the circuit (by a battery or by the mains supply) and upon the *resistance* which the circuit offers to the passage of electrons through it. Current, voltage and resistance are related by three equations which are commonly referred to as Ohm's Law:

$$I = \frac{V}{R} \qquad V = I \times R \qquad R = \frac{V}{I}$$

where I stands for current in amps, V stands for voltage and R stands for resistance in ohms.

A lamp whose filament has a resistance of 6 ohms is connected to a 12-volt battery. What current flows? The equation $I = \frac{V}{R}$ gives the result immediately since $I = \frac{12 \text{ volts}}{6 \text{ ohms}} = 2$ amps. If an exactly similar lamp is added to the circuit so that the current has to flow through both of them in turn, what current flows? The voltage of the battery cannot change so V = 12. But the resistance has been doubled. The two separate lamps, *wired in series*, as this method of connection is called, are equivalent to a single lamp with a double-length filament. So R = 12 ohms. Putting these values in the equation $I = \frac{V}{R}$ gives $I = \frac{12 \text{ volts}}{12 \text{ ohms}} = 1$ amp. In other words the current has been halved and as a result the lamps only glow dimly.

The same pair of lamps can be *wired in parallel,* i.e. side by side so that the current is divided between them,

part of the current going through the first lamp and the remainder going through the other. With this system of wiring it is found that both lamps glow as brightly as the single lamp in the first experiment. The current flowing through the single lamp in the first experiment was 2 amps, so the current flowing through each of the two lamps wired in parallel is also 2 amps. The *total* current supplied by the 12-volt battery is therefore 4 amps. Putting these values in the equation $R = \frac{V}{I}$ indicates that the *total* resistance of the circuit is $\frac{12 \text{ volts}}{4 \text{ amps}} = 3$ ohms. It may seem sur-

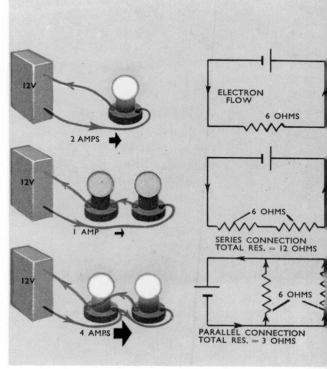

2 AMPS

1 AMP

4 AMPS

ELECTRON FLOW

6 OHMS

6 OHMS

SERIES CONNECTION
TOTAL RES. = 12 OHMS

6 OHMS

PARALLEL CONNECTION
TOTAL RES. = 3 OHMS

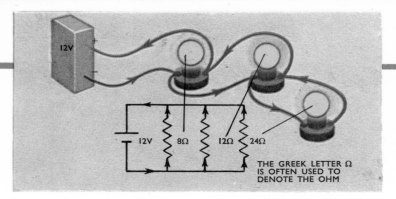

THE GREEK LETTER Ω IS OFTEN USED TO DENOTE THE OHM

Total current in parallel circuits equals sum of currents flowing through each lamp, i.e.,

$$I = \frac{V}{R} = \frac{12}{R} = \frac{12}{8} + \frac{12}{12} + \frac{12}{24} \text{ hence } \frac{I}{R} = \frac{I}{8} + \frac{I}{12} + \frac{I}{24} \text{ where } R \text{ is combined resis-}$$

tance of lamps.

When components are wired in parallel the same voltage is applied to each of them. In a simple circuit consisting of several lamps wired in parallel and a battery to drive current through them, each lamp is directly linked to the battery terminals. If a 12 volt battery is used then the voltage drop across each lamp, no matter what its resistance, is plainly 12 volts. The current flowing through each lamp will depend upon its resistance, and the current will divide equally only if all the lamps have identical resistances.

Suppose that a circuit consists simply of a 12 volt battery and three lamps of resistance 8 ohms, 12 ohms and 24 ohms wired in parallel. The current flowing through the 8 ohms lamp is $\frac{12 \text{ volts}}{8 \text{ ohms}} = \frac{12}{8}$ amps (since $I = \frac{V}{R}$ from Ohm's Law). The current flowing through the 12 ohms lamp is $\frac{12 \text{ volts}}{12 \text{ ohms}} = \frac{12}{12}$ amps and the current flowing through the 24 ohms lamp is $\frac{12 \text{ volts}}{24 \text{ ohms}} = \frac{12}{24}$ amps. Hence the total current supplied by the battery is $\frac{12}{8} + \frac{12}{12} + \frac{12}{24}$ amps.

The effective resistance (R ohms) of the three lamps is the resistance of the single lamp which would draw the same current from the battery. The Ohm's Law equation $I = \frac{V}{R}$ indicates that the current drawn from a 12 volt battery by a resistance of R ohms is $\frac{12}{R}$. From the meaning of the term effective resistance this current is the same as the total current supplied to the three separate lamps. Hence $\frac{12}{R} = \frac{12}{8} + \frac{12}{12} + \frac{12}{24}$.

Dividing both sides of the equation by 12 gives $\frac{I}{R} = \frac{I}{8} + \frac{I}{12} + \frac{I}{24}$

This equation can be applied to any three resistances wired in parallel by writing their values in place of the 8, 12, and 24 used in this particular example. If the first resistance is r_1 ohms, the second r_2 ohms, and the third r_3 ohms the equation becomes $\frac{I}{R} = \frac{I}{r_1} + \frac{I}{r_2} + \frac{I}{r_3}$ *which is the formula for finding the effective value of three resistances in parallel. Where there are, for example, five resistances wired in parallel, instead of three, the formula for finding the effective resistance, R, becomes* $\frac{I}{R} = \frac{I}{r_1} + \frac{I}{r_2} + \frac{I}{r_3} + \frac{I}{r_4} + \frac{I}{r_5}$

In just the same way the formula can be extended to cover any number of resistances.

The lamps whose resistances are 8 ohms, 12 ohms and 24 ohms used in the example above have an effective resistance R ohms given by the equation

$$\frac{I}{R} = \frac{I}{8} + \frac{I}{12} + \frac{I}{24} = \frac{3}{24} + \frac{2}{24} + \frac{I}{24} = \frac{6}{24} = \frac{I}{4}$$

Since $\frac{I}{R} = \frac{I}{4}$ then $R = 4$ ohms

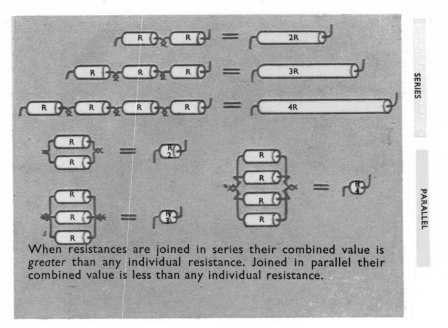

When resistances are joined in series their combined value is *greater* than any individual resistance. Joined in parallel their combined value is less than any individual resistance.

prising that two lamps together can have a smaller resistance than a single lamp. But the two lamps in parallel are equivalent to a single lamp with a double-thickness filament, and the thicker the filament the less the resistance, for a current passes more easily through a thick wire than a thin one.

The *total* resistance of a number of lamps or other components wired in *series* is found by adding together the resistances of the separate components. If the resistances of the various components wired in series are r_1, r_2, r_3, etc., then the total resistance, R, is given by the formula:

$$R = r_1 + r_2 + r_3 +$$

The *effective* resistance of a number of components wired in *parallel* is found by using the formula:

$$\frac{1}{R} = \frac{1}{r_1} + \frac{1}{r_2} + \frac{1}{r_3} +$$

Where R is the effective resistance of the whole circuit, and r_1, r_2, r_3, etc., are the resistances of the separate components.

In the experiment mentioned earlier where two lamps were wired in parallel the separate resistances r_1 and r_2 were each 6 ohms. Putting these values into the formula for resistances in parallel gives:

$$\frac{1}{R} = \frac{1}{r_1} + \frac{1}{r_2} = \frac{1}{6} + \frac{1}{6} = \frac{2}{6} = \frac{1}{3}$$

So $\frac{1}{R} = \frac{1}{3}$ and therefore R = 3 ohms.

The *effective* resistance of the two lamps is 3 ohms – the same result as that indicated by the experiment.

Electric lamps are nearly always wired in parallel for two reasons. First, each lamp can be provided with a switch of its own so that it can be switched on or off without affecting the other lamps. In the case of a series circuit, if one lamp breaks or is switched off the whole circuit is broken and all the lamps go out. Second, lamps wired in parallel have a smaller total of effective resistance than the same number of lamps wired in series.

CHAPTER FOUR

Resistance and Voltage Drop

WHENEVER an electric current flows through a circuit, it meets with a certain amount of resistance. The voltage, resistance and current are related by Ohm's Law;

Voltage = resistance × current.

'Voltage' in Ohm's Law stands for *voltage difference*. If, for example, a battery is pushing the current around the circuit, then its two terminals are at different voltages. In other words, there is a *voltage difference* between them.

But voltage difference is not just something that 'happens' at the battery terminals. In fact, the voltage changes continuously throughout the circuit. A very simple electric circuit may consist of a 2 volt battery and a length of uniform resistance wire. The voltage of one of the terminals is 2 volts higher than the other. It is, say, at 2 volts, and the other is at 0 volts (*Earth*). Along the wire, the voltage drops uniformly. At quarter-way round the circuit, the voltage has dropped to 1·5 volts. At half-way it is down to 1 volt, at the three-quarters

mark it is only 0·5 volts, and at the other end, the battery terminal, it is down to 0 volts.

The voltage drop around a circuit is like the drop in pressure as water is forced through a narrow pipe, or the drop in potential energy of water as it flows downhill. Half-way down the hill, its potential energy is half-way between its values at the top and the bottom.

The voltage drop across a resistance is utilized in the *voltage* or *potential divider*. The voltage difference between the terminals of the power source may be 100 volts. But any voltage differences between 0 and 100 can be obtained by connecting a resistor across the 100 volt power supply, and 'tapping off', at a point along the resistor, the required voltage. For instance, the voltage difference between one of the supply terminals and the middle of the resistor is 50 volts. Potential divider resistors are normally equipped with 'tapping off' terminals so that the circuit to be supplied with current can be connected to them.

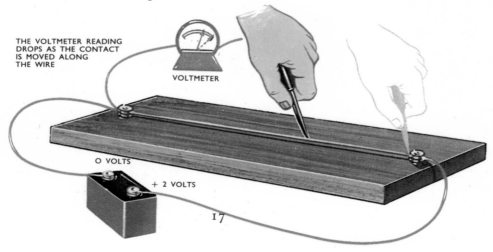

THE VOLTMETER READING
DROPS AS THE CONTACT
IS MOVED ALONG
THE WIRE

VOLTMETER

0 VOLTS

+ 2 VOLTS

Three Ways of looking at voltage difference

HIGH PRESSURE   LOWER PRESSURE   LOWEST PRESSURE

1. The voltage difference as the difference in electric pressure.
The current is likened to the flow of water through a pipe. A difference in pressure between two points pushes the current along the pipe. In a circuit, a battery supplies a difference in electric pressure by putting an excess of electrons on to one part of the circuit, and creating a lack of electrons in another part.

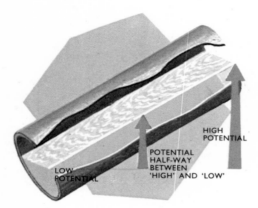

HIGH POTENTIAL

POTENTIAL HALF-WAY BETWEEN 'HIGH' AND 'LOW'

LOW POTENTIAL

2. The voltage difference as the difference in potential.
Potential is a shortened form of *potential energy*. The current is like the downhill flow of water through a pipe. Current flows because water at one end of the pipe is higher than the other end – in other words – because it has a higher potential energy (energy of position). In an electrical circuit, a difference in potential energy is maintained between the two battery terminals.

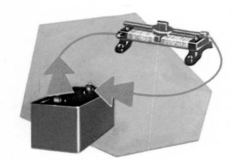

3. The voltage difference as the electromotive force (e.m.f.).
Difference in electrical pressure, or difference in potential, can apply between any two points in a circuit. But electromotive force (which means quite literally the force moving electrons) is usually reserved for the source of electric power, the battery. It is a measure of the amount of energy the battery supplies to the circuit, and is again measured in volts.

An electric current is a flow of electrons, which are being pumped from one end of the resistor to the other. Electrons starting from one end of the resistor must leave it via the other end: the current is therefore the same through all parts of the resistor.

From Ohm's law, the current is equal to $\dfrac{voltage}{resistance} = \dfrac{100}{100} = 1$ amp.

The current through each half is exactly the same – 1 amp. So, again from Ohm's law, the voltage across each half is   current × resistance = 1 × 50 = 50 volts.

ELECTRON FLOW   0 VOLTS   50 OHMS   50 VOLTS   50 OHMS   + 100 VOLTS   ELECTRON FLOW

CURRENT = 1 AMP

CHAPTER FIVE

Specific Resistance

OHM'S law states that the ratio of the voltage between the ends of an electrical conductor to the current flowing through it is a constant. For a given conductor this constant is called the *resistance*. In other words $\frac{voltage}{current}$ = resistance. The resistance is an indication of how much opposition the flow of electrons meets in its attempt to pass through the conductor.

Materials which conduct electricity may be classified as 'good' conductors if they offer a low resistance, and 'bad' conductors if they offer a high resistance. Copper, for example, is used for almost all electrical wiring because it is a 'good' conductor. However, a copper wire can have a very high resistance, perhaps a million ohms, if it is made long enough and thin enough. This does not mean that copper is a bad conductor; it simply means that when considering resistance, the *dimensions* of the conductor must be taken into account as well as the material from which it is made.

If the flow of electrons through a conductor is compared with the flow of water through a pipe, it is fairly easy to see that just as a long pipe offers a greater opposition to the water than does a short pipe, so a long wire offers a greater resistance to the electrons than does a short wire. Similarly, just as a wide pipe offers less opposition to the water than does a narrow pipe, so a thick wire offers less resistance to the electrons than does a thin wire. The longer the wire, the greater is its resistance; the thicker the wire the smaller is its resistance.

In fact for any wire the resistance, R (measured in ohms), is related to the length, l (measured in centimetres), and the area of cross-section A (measured in square centimetres), by the equation:

$$R = \frac{\varrho \times l}{A},$$

where ϱ is a number that depends on the material of which the wire is made. This number, ϱ, is called the *specific resistance* or *resistivity* of the material. In the case of copper, for example, $\varrho = 0.00000178$ ohm-centimetres (*not* ohms per centimetre).

Copper	**Brass**	**Eureka or Constantan**	**Tungsten**
$\varrho = 0.00000178$ ohm-cm.	$\varrho = 0.000006$ ohm-cm.	(an alloy of 40% nickel, 60% copper) $\varrho = 0.000049$ ohm-cm.	$\varrho = 0.0000046$ ohm-cm.
Copper has a very low resistivity and is used for all kinds of electrical wiring.	Brass has low resistivity and is used for the parts of a circuit which have to be mechanically strong.	Eureka has a fairly high resistivity. It is used in wire-wound resistors.	Tungsten has a fairly high resistivity. It is used for the filaments of lamps and tubes (valves) (because it has a high melting point).

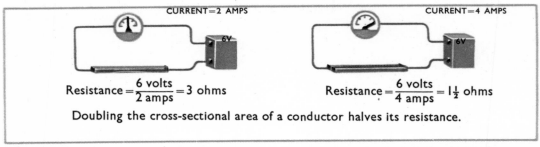

$$\text{Resistance} = \frac{6 \text{ volts}}{2 \text{ amps}} = 3 \text{ ohms}$$

$$\text{Resistance} = \frac{6 \text{ volts}}{4 \text{ amps}} = 1\tfrac{1}{2} \text{ ohms}$$

Doubling the cross-sectional area of a conductor halves its resistance.

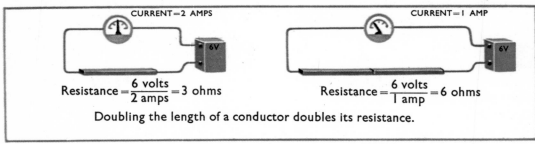

CURRENT=2 AMPS   CURRENT=1 AMP

$$\text{Resistance} = \frac{6 \text{ volts}}{2 \text{ amps}} = 3 \text{ ohms}$$

$$\text{Resistance} = \frac{6 \text{ volts}}{1 \text{ amp}} = 6 \text{ ohms}$$

Doubling the length of a conductor doubles its resistance.

These specimens of different metals have equal resistances. The resistance of a conductor depends on its dimensions as well as the material of which it is made.

For silver $\varrho = 0\cdot00000163$ ohm-centimetres, so the specific resistance of silver is less than that of copper, and silver is therefore a better conductor than copper.

The *specific resistance* or *resistivity* of a material is quite independent of the dimensions of whatever specimen of the material is being considered. But it can be thought of as the resistance between opposite faces of a cube of the material one centimetre long, one centimetre wide and one centimetre deep (i.e. about the size and shape of a dice).

To find the specific resistance or resistivity of a specimen, say a wire, it is necessary to measure its resistance R, its length l and area of cross-section A, so that ϱ can be obtained from the equation $R = \dfrac{\varrho \times l}{A}$. The resistance ($R$) is usually measured by means of a Wheatstone Bridge.

Since wires are nearly always circular in section, the area of cross-section (A) is generally found by measuring the diameter of the wire with the aid of a micrometer screw gauge. Half the diameter is the radius r, and the area of cross-section is given by the formula πr^2.

CHAPTER SIX

The Potentiometer

THE voltage or potential difference between two points in an electric circuit may be measured by a voltmeter. But although voltmeters are very convenient in use, they have one serious disadvantage in accurate work – they draw a small current from the main circuit. A better, though somewhat more elaborate, apparatus, which measures voltage *without* drawing a current from the circuit, is the *potentiometer*.

The essential feature of a potentiometer is a length of uniform resistance wire which is stretched across a board. An electric current from an accumulator or other fairly constant voltage source flows along this wire. Since the wire is uniform, it may be regarded as a number of equal resistances in series (equal length sections have equal resistance).

For instance, a potentiometer wire one metre long consists of ten sections each ten centimetres long and each having a resistance of $\frac{1}{10}$ the total resistance of the whole wire. When a steady current flows along the wire, the voltage drop or potential difference across one section is $\frac{1}{10}$ that across the whole wire. The potential difference across two sections is $\frac{2}{10}$ the total and across three sections is $\frac{3}{10}$ the total.

The wire is, of course, continuous, so for this purpose may be divided into

As the tapping key is moved from left to right along the potentiometer wire, the reading on the voltmeter increases. The deflection on the voltmeter is doubled (i.e. the potential difference is doubled) by moving the tapping key from the 40 cm to the 80 cm mark. The voltage drop or potential difference across a certain length of wire is proportional to that length.

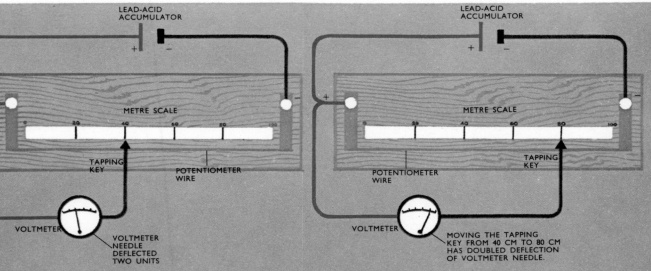

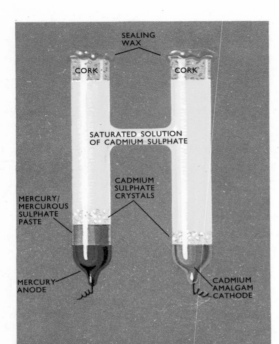

SEALING WAX

CORK

CORK

SATURATED SOLUTION
OF CADMIUM SULPHATE

CADMIUM
SULPHATE
CRYSTALS

MERCURY/
MERCUROUS
SULPHATE
PASTE

MERCURY
ANODE

CADMIUM
AMALGAM
CATHODE

Weston Standard Cell

This cell is frequently used as an accurate standard of electromotive force (or potential difference) for calibrating potentiometers. As shown in the diagram, the cell is housed in an H-shaped glass vessel. The pure mercury at the foot of one limb acts as the positive electrode (*anode*), while the negative electrode (*cathode*) consists of cadmium amalgam containing between 12% and 14% by weight of cadmium. Short platinum wires are fused into the feet of the two limbs to provide external connections for the actual electrodes. The electrolyte is a *saturated solution* of cadmium sulphate while the mercurous sulphate paste on the pure mercury anode acts as a *depolarizer*.

Provided these cells are used carefully they maintain their electromotive force (1·0183V at 20°C) for many years.

any convenient number of equal sections. The outcome of the reasoning will always be the same, namely that the potential difference across a certain length of the wire is proportional to that length. Thus if the potential difference across one section is 0·6 volts and across a larger section is 1·2 volt, the second section is twice as long as the first.

This may be shown experimentally by attaching one terminal of a voltmeter to one end of the potentiometer wire, while a *tapping key* is attached to the other terminal. By means of this key, electrical contact can be made at any point along the wire. As the key is moved further along the wire (away from the end to which the first terminal is attached), the reading on the voltmeter increases. In this instance, a small current flows from the main circuit into the voltmeter circuit.

When the potentiometer wire is to be used in making measurements, a cell is inserted in the voltmeter circuit and the voltmeter replaced by a galvanometer, since the latter instrument is more sensitive in detecting small currents. The two current sources (the original accumulator and the new cell in the 'voltmeter circuit') are arranged so that the positive terminal of each is attached to the same end of the potentiometer wire.

Provided that the total potential difference or voltage drop along the potentiometer wire is greater than the voltage of the cell in the voltmeter circuit, a point can be found along the wire for which no current flows through the galvanometer. At this point, the potential difference (or drop in voltage) across that section of the potentiometer is equal in size to the pressure difference caused by the cell, but these two potential

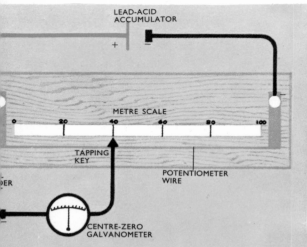

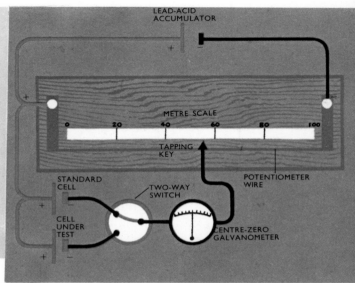

Lead-acid accumulators maintain a fairly constant e.m.f. of 2.1 volts per cell until almost completely discharged. They may, therefore, be used as a standard in potentiometer work if a high degree of accuracy is not required. This circuit may be used for comparing the e.m.f. of a cell with that of an accumulator.

For really accurate work the potentiometer wire has first to be calibrated using the Weston Standard cell. Only then may the e.m.f. of the other cell be measured. These determinations may be made rapidly by having a two-way switch in this circuit.

differences oppose each other. As a consequence no current flows through the galvanometer and so this gives a zero reading. However, if the tapping key is moved slightly to either side of this *balance point*, a small current flows through the meter.

If the potential difference of a cell or other current source is to be measured, this is done by comparing its potential with that of a *standard cell* whose voltage is known accurately. The standard cell is put into the circuit first and by means of it the potentiometer wire is

calibrated. As a consequence, it may be found that 1 cm. of the wire is equivalent to $0 \cdot 031$ V. Then a new balance point is found using the cell of unknown voltage. A balance point at $52 \cdot 5$ cm. indicates a voltage of $0 \cdot 031 \times 52 \cdot 5 = 1 \cdot 63$ V.

The potentiometer is, essentially a device for comparing voltages. However, as current, voltage and resistance are linked with one another in Ohm's law, the potentiometer can also be used to compare currents and resistances.

CHAPTER SEVEN

The Heating Effect of a Current

WHENEVER an electric current passes through a conducting wire a certain amount of heat is produced. The heat is generated as the current strives to overcome the resistance of the wire. The electrical resistance of any substance is the opposition it offers to a flow of electricity through it. Since an electric current is a flow of electrons jumping from atom to atom along a conducting wire, the resistance of a substance depends basically upon how tightly electrons are held to atoms. In a good conductor of electricity, such as copper, some of the electrons are only loosely held to atoms and the resistance is very low, while in a poor conductor of electricity (an insulator) such as rubber, all of the electrons are held very tightly to atoms and the resistance is very high indeed. But for any one metal its resistance depends chiefly upon its thickness and length. The thicker it is the less the resistance, and *vice versa*, while the longer it is the greater the resistance, and *vice versa*.

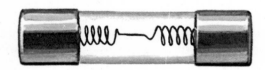

The wire in a fuse is made from some metal or alloy which has a low melting point. If too large a current flows through the circuit sufficient heat is generated to melt the fuse wire. This breaks the circuit and prevents more serious damage.

The amount of heat produced depends upon three factors: the size of the current, the length of time it is passed through the conducting wire, and the resistance of the wire. There is a very simple formula for finding the exact amount of heat that will be obtained by passing a certain current through a certain wire for a certain length of time. It is I^2Rt, where I represents the current in amps (I^2 means multiplying the current by itself), R the resistance of the wire in ohms and t the length of time in seconds. The answer is the amount of heat produced in *joules*. These units were named after the scientist who discovered this simple rule, James Joule (1818–1889). To change joules into *calories* (a calorie is the amount of heat needed to raise the temperature of one gram of water by one degree centigrade) you simply divide by 4·18 (4·18 joules are equivalent to one calorie).

The heating effect of a current has many practical uses. One of its most valuable applications is in the light bulb. This contains a long, very thin tungsten wire filament which offers a considerable resistance to the flow of electricity through it (the wire may be as much as two feet in length though wound into a coil less than one inch in length). The formula shows that the greater the resistance of the conducting wire the greater the heat produced. In this case sufficient heat is produced to make the wire filament glow white hot—hence the light. The theory behind the light

bulb seems very simple, but in fact
early manufacturers faced a number
of problems. It took a long search, for
instance, to find a material suitable
for the filament. Thomas Alva Edison,
the American inventor of the first
successful incandescent bulb (1879),
used charred bamboo for this purpose
at first. He also solved the problem
of keeping the filament from burning
(combining chemically with the oxygen in the air) by sealing it in a glass
bulb from which he pumped out the
air. But even in later vacuum bulbs,
where a tungsten filament was used,
the metal slowly vaporized and was
deposited as a dark coating on the inside of the bulb. To prevent this most
bulbs are now filled with an inert
(unreactive) gas such as argon which
does not react chemically with tungsten and by being present prevents
the metal from vaporizing.

Electric fires work on the same
principle as the electric light. An
electric current is passed through a
coil of wire. The wire offers a
considerable resistance to the flow
of electricity through it and sufficient heat is generated as the current
overcomes this resistance to make the
filament glow red hot. The wire then
not only heats the air but also sends
out radiant heat (heat rays). The
filament is wound on a support which
does not conduct electricity (an insulator), and since the material used
for the support must also be able to
withstand high temperatures, mica or
fireclay is normally used. The metal
of the filament is usually an alloy
of nickel and chromium. Most other
metals would oxidize (combine with
the oxygen in the air) and burn out
too quickly. Immersion heaters for
heating water are constructed in a
similar way to electric fires, but in this
case the filament must be encased to
avoid contact with the water.

Fuses, used to protect electrical circuits, represent another useful application of the heating effect of a
current. If, for some reason, a
greater current passes through an
appliance than is intended, the element is liable to heat up tremendously
and melt. This might happen if two
bare wires touched and the current
was able to take a short cut and bypass
much of the planned resistance. This
state of affairs is prevented by inserting a fuse in the circuit at some

point. This is simply a fine piece of wire which has a much lower melting point than the rest of the circuit. If the current flowing through the circuit becomes greater than it should be, the thin fuse wire becomes so hot that it melts, thus breaking the circuit and preventing more serious damage to the appliance.

An important industrial application is in electrical furnaces and kilns (a furnace is an apparatus for melting metals). The *resistance furnace* operates on the same lines as the domestic electric heater, but on a grander scale. The *arc furnace*, like the *arc lamp*, utilizes the fact that if two carbon rods (called electrodes), with a large current passing through them, are slightly separated the current does not cease to flow, for a small spark jumps between them. The result is an arc of intense white light. Great heat is produced because air offers a tremendous resistance to the flow of electricity through it, and the greater the resistance the greater the heat produced by the passage of a current. Normally speaking, air is an insulator, but if the gap in the circuit (i.e. the length of air through which the electricity has to flow) is small enough and the voltage (the electrical pressure) high enough, this resistance can be overcome. In some arc furnaces the metal is melted by the heat of an arc between two carbon electrodes held in position above it. In others the metal itself is made to act as a companion electrode to a carbon rod and is melted by the heat of the arc.

CHAPTER EIGHT

The Reason most Countries have an Electric Grid

ELECTRICITY plays an important role in practically every home. Lamps, radiograms, television sets, electric fires, doorbells, irons, immersion heaters, washing machines, electric cookers and refrigerators and many other domestic appliances are worked by electrical energy. Outside the home it is equally important. Electric railways, traffic lights and street lighting are all part of our everyday lives. And less obvious, though even more important, is the fact that nearly every object you handle has been made either wholly or in part by electrically operated machines.

This widespread demand for electricity only started in the closing years of the last century, after the invention

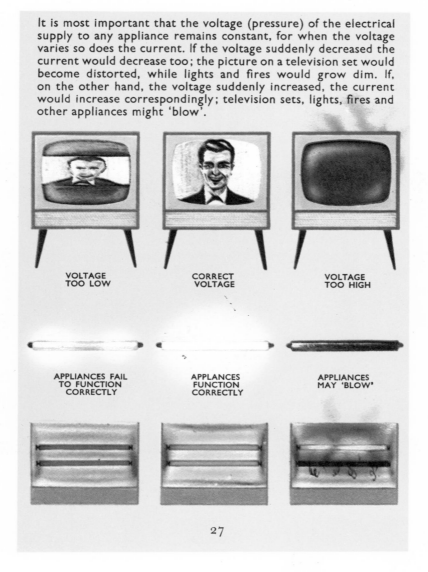

It is most important that the voltage (pressure) of the electrical supply to any appliance remains constant, for when the voltage varies so does the current. If the voltage suddenly decreased the current would decrease too; the picture on a television set would become distorted, while lights and fires would grow dim. If, on the other hand, the voltage suddenly increased, the current would increase correspondingly; television sets, lights, fires and other appliances might 'blow'.

VOLTAGE TOO LOW CORRECT VOLTAGE VOLTAGE TOO HIGH

APPLIANCES FAIL TO FUNCTION CORRECTLY APPLANCES FUNCTION CORRECTLY APPLIANCES MAY 'BLOW' of the incandescent filament lamp. At that time most of the electrical power used was produced either chemically (by batteries) or by single generators, many of which were privately owned. The natural result of the vastly increased demand was the building of central power stations, where the great amount of electrical power needed could be produced most efficiently. And with this came the network of power lines carrying the electric current from the generating stations to consumers in (eventually) almost every part of the country, and linking the power stations themselves. These are the lines which, supported by large pylons placed some 300 yards apart, run for miles across the countryside. This is the *grid system*.

One of the most important features of the grid system is that it ensures that the current is always supplied to the consumer at a constant 'pressure' or voltage. If the voltage of the consumer's electrical supply increased for some reason and the resistance (the radio, television, etc.) remained constant, the current strength would increase correspondingly. The result of this could be drastic. At the very least, every fuse in the house would 'blow'. If, on the other hand, the voltage decreased, the current strength would fall, too. In this case, lamp bulbs would grow dim and many appliances fail to function at all. Now this drop in voltage is exactly what is likely to happen at 'peak periods' when so many appliances are in operation that the electrical power is being used faster than the generators at the power station can produce it. It is rather like a number of pipes leading off a reservoir. If the water is allowed to flow away through more and more

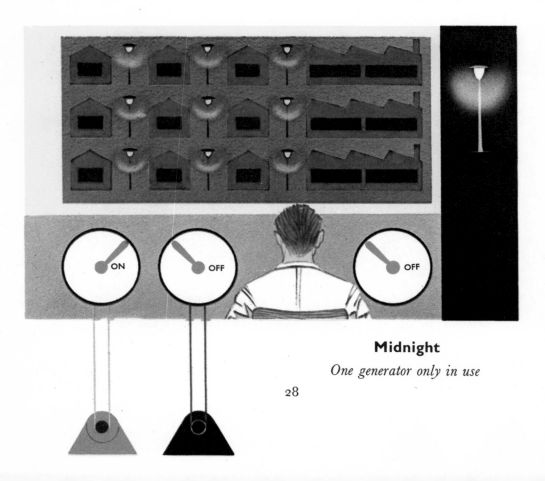

Midnight

One generator only in use

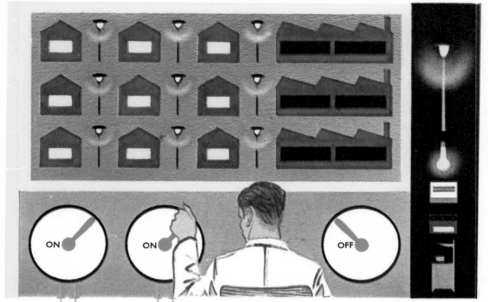

8 p.m.

Two generators in use

During the night one generator can handle the demand for electrical power. In the evening two generators are needed to meet the consumers' demands.

8 a.m. is one of the peak periods when both generators together cannot produce sufficient electrical power to meet the demand and more electrical energy must be brought in through the grid system from an outside generator.

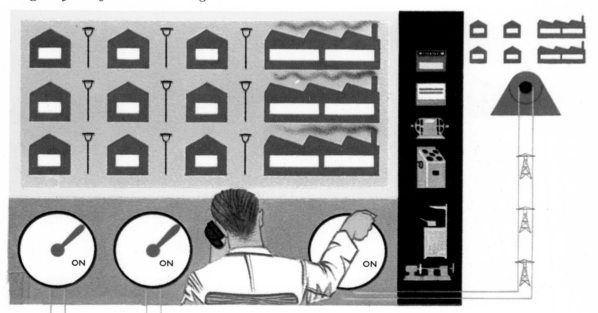

8 a.m.

Extra electrical power must be brought in

29

pipes the level in the reservoir will fall; consequently the pressure at which the water is pushed out through the pipes will fall and likewise the rate at which the water flows (current strength).

The awkward thing about electricity is that, unlike water or gas, it cannot be stored. It is not possible to form a reservoir of surplus electrical energy generated when there is little demand for it (in the middle of the night, for instance), which can be drawn upon when demand exceeds production (during the peak periods, around 8 a.m. and 6 p.m.). The very nature of electricity makes it impossible to store. It is simply a flow of electrons brought about by the unnatural state of atoms at one end of a conducting wire having a surplus of electrons while those at the other end have less than their share. This state is only momentary, for a flow of electrons (an electric current) immediately corrects it and *at the same time* can be made to do work. A continuous current is achieved by ensuring that this unnatural state is kept up despite the flow of electrons.

As electricity cannot be stored the only way to maintain a steady voltage during peak periods is to bring in additional generators. This is just what the grid system makes possible. When the generators of one power station become overloaded electrical power is supplied through the grid system from another station where the generators are not overloaded. What happens in practice is that generators in the largest power stations, where electrical energy is produced most economically, are kept running at full power the whole time, while the smaller, less efficient stations are only switched in during a peak period

and closed down when it has passed. Which station should be switched in and when is decided at a number of regional control centres. Thus it is the grid system which has made it possible for an electric current to be supplied to all consumers at a steady voltage at all times of the day.

The greatest problem provided by the establishment of central power stations was the distribution of the current over the many miles of power lines. Electrical power, measured in watts, is the product of electrical potential in volts and current strength in amps. Thus, for instance, 100 watts equals 100 volts multiplied by 1 amp. But 100 watts also equals 1 volt multiplied by 100 amps and 2 volts multiplied by 50 amps. This means that there are two ways in which a certain amount of electrical power may be transmitted from one place to another; either as a large current at a low voltage or a small current at a high voltage. The first method is very wasteful because a large current loses much of its energy in overcoming the resistance of the wire (the 'lost' energy is transformed into heat). The second method is far better economically, for with a very large voltage the current can be very small and very little energy will be lost in heating the wires. This method, used almost universally today for the long-distance transmission of electrical energy, involves the use of transformers. The voltage at the generating station is stepped up by a transformer to the 132 thousand volts or so maintained in the grid system. This is far too high to be of use in the home, so at the consumers' end of the grid it is stepped down again by another transformer (or series of transformers) to the standard voltage of the domestic mains.

Magnetism and
Electromagnetism

CHAPTER NINE

Magnets and Magnetism

THE 'LOVES' AND 'HATES' OF MAGNETS

A magnet is a piece of iron, steel or lodestone ore which attracts to itself other pieces of iron. Every magnet has two poles (in the case of the bar magnet they are at either end of it), from which magnetic forces seem to operate. The north poles are attracted to the south poles of other magnets, but 'hate' the other norths. Similarly the souths 'like' norths, but are repelled by the other souths. Briefly put: *unlike poles attract each other; like poles repel each other.*

Perhaps the best known practical instance of this attraction between unlike poles occurs in our magnetic compasses. The Earth, we know, is a vast magnet and the compass needle a very small one. One pole (end) of the compass needle always points to the Earth's Magnetic North Pole; the other will never do so. The use of magnetism would seem from this to be limited to people like explorers and sailors who need to find the direction of North by a compass. But magnetism is a curious force, its most important action for us is that it enables electricity to be made by mechanical means.

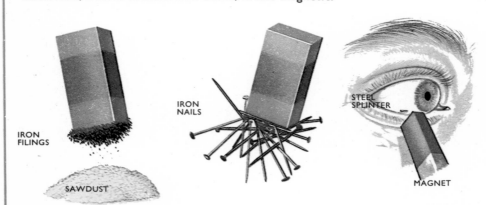

Magnets are pieces of iron which are capable of attracting other pieces of iron. The metals cobalt and nickel are also capable of doing this but to a much smaller extent. Lodestone, a form of black iron oxide, is also magnetic.

IRON FILINGS

SAWDUST

IRON NAILS

STEEL SPLINTER

MAGNET

(*Left*) Magnet separates iron filings (iron dust) from a heap of the filings mixed with sawdust. Magnets can be used for picking up small iron or steel objects such as pins or removing splinters of these metals from someone's eye.

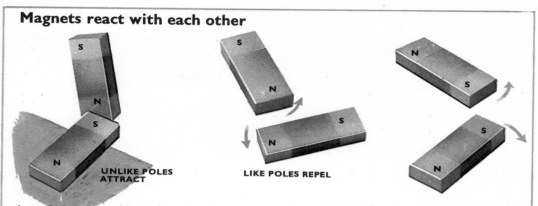

Magnets react with each other

UNLIKE POLES ATTRACT

LIKE POLES REPEL

It is always the unlike poles of a magnet that attract each other, *i.e.* a north pole attracts a south pole. The two magnets have to be pulled apart. Poles which are alike – either two north poles or two south poles – repel each other. They move to avoid coming into contact.

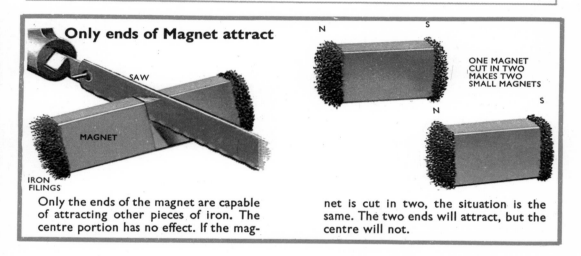

Only ends of Magnet attract

SAW

MAGNET

IRON FILINGS

ONE MAGNET CUT IN TWO MAKES TWO SMALL MAGNETS

Only the ends of the magnet are capable of attracting other pieces of iron. The centre portion has no effect. If the mag-

net is cut in two, the situation is the same. The two ends will attract, but the centre will not.

ONE MAGNET MAKES ANOTHER

A magnet has the power to attract to it pieces of iron, steel, nickel or cobalt. The force of attraction is called magnetism. When a bar magnet is moved towards an iron nail, the nail is attracted to it. Why should this be? Because the nail comes into the influence of the magnetic force it is made temporarily into another magnet and behaves like one. The force of attraction is greatest from the ends or *poles* of the magnet. There is little attraction from its middle. One end of the magnet is called a south

or 'south seeking' pole, the other end is a north or 'north seeking' pole. If the south pole is moved towards the nail, the end of the nail which is nearest to the magnet becomes, temporarily, a north pole. Since among all magnets unlike poles attract, the nail is drawn to the end of the magnet. The other end of the nail becomes a south pole. With the nail hanging to the magnet it is possible to pick up several more nails in a line, for the first nail itself is acting as a magnet. The end of the second nail which is

A simple Theory of Magnetism

An ordinary piece of iron is made up of small magnets joined end to end in closed rings so that there are no spare unattached ends. Each magnet has neutralised the effect of its neighbours.

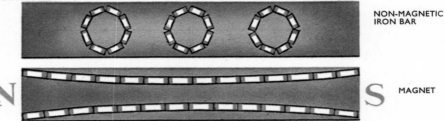

NON-MAGNETIC
IRON BAR

N   S   MAGNET

In a magnet, the rings of magnets have been drawn into lines. At one end of a line there is a free unattached north pole which is free to attract iron outside the magnet itself At the other end is a free south pole.

touching the first nail will be a north pole and the far end a south pole, and so on along the line of nails. In fact, each of the nails becomes a magnet itself while it is affected by the actual magnet.

Two magnets are produced by cutting one in half and the process can be repeated by halving the pieces again and again. A magnet is, in fact, made up of a large number of infinitely smaller magnets. If you partly fill a test tube with iron filings you can see that the filings are arranged haphazardly. If you then hold the tube still and move a magnet from one end to the other, using the same pole of the magnet all the time and moving

Simple Ways of making Magnets

Weak magnets can be made by repeatedly stroking a piece of iron with one end of a magnet. The stroking must be always in the same direction. This has the effect of breaking the closed rings and dragging the small magnets into line. Soft iron is easier to magnetise than hard steel.

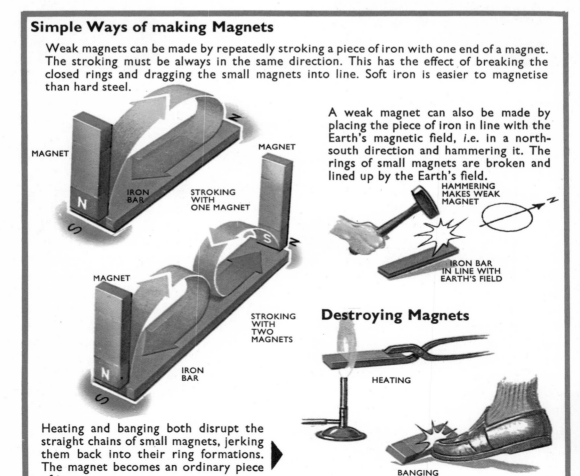

MAGNET

IRON BAR

STROKING WITH ONE MAGNET

MAGNET

MAGNET

STROKING WITH TWO MAGNETS

IRON BAR

A weak magnet can also be made by placing the piece of iron in line with the Earth's magnetic field, i.e. in a north-south direction and hammering it. The rings of small magnets are broken and lined up by the Earth's field.

HAMMERING MAKES WEAK MAGNET

IRON BAR IN LINE WITH EARTH'S FIELD

Destroying Magnets

HEATING

BANGING

Heating and banging both disrupt the straight chains of small magnets, jerking them back into their ring formations. The magnet becomes an ordinary piece of iron.

the magnet only in one direction along the test tube, the iron filings will arrange themselves along the tube *all* pointing the same way. The whole mass of iron filings in the tube will act in the way that a simple bar magnet does. One end of the test tube will be repelled by the south pole of a magnet, the other by the north pole.

The molecules in an unmagnetised bar of iron are haphazardly arranged like the iron filings in the test tube. Each is a tiny magnet and when a piece of lodestone (a natural magnetic rock) is stroked from one end of the iron bar to the other, using, say, the *north* pole of the lodestone, the south poles of the molecules will all be turned in the direction that the lode-stone is moved along the iron bar. The south pole and the north pole of the nearest neighbouring molecules will attract each other (unlike poles attract) all the way along the piece of iron so that they will be arranged in a NSNSNSNS chain like nails are when they are picked up by a magnet.

At the end of the iron on which the lodestone is placed the very last molecules will have their north poles facing outwards, so that end of the iron will be the new magnet's north pole. At the end of the iron from which the lodestone was taken away, the very last molecules will have their south poles facing outwards, so that end of the iron will be the south pole.

MAGNETIC FIELD

The power of attraction of a magnet is called magnetism. Any region near a magnet where the effects of magnetism (such as the deflection of a compass needle) can be detected is called a *magnetic field*.

The field around a bar magnet can be seen as a pattern if a sheet of paper is laid over it and sprinkled with iron filings. The filings will move into lines when the paper is tapped. These 'lines of force', as they are called, show the path which a single north magnetic pole would take if it was free to move. The lines of force seem to begin on a north pole and end on a south pole. They represent the direction of the magnetic field. What they do not show, however, is that the magnetic field extends all round the magnet. The paper only shows the magnetic field in one plane.

When a horseshoe magnet is laid flat underneath a piece of paper on which iron filings are scattered a similar pattern is obtained between the two poles with a less distinct pattern around the base of the 'U'. Lines of force are crowded together between the poles, because the field there is intense.

When two bar magnets are placed near each other with the north of one next to the south of the other (two unlike poles) and the paper on which iron filings are scattered is placed above and tapped, the filings form a pattern in which the lines of force are shown passing between the two poles (attraction). But when the two south poles or the two north poles are nearest each other (two like poles) the lines of force pass away from each other and swing at right angles away from the magnets (repulsion), leaving a space between the poles where there are no lines of force and no magnetic field.

Magnetic Field

Every magnet has a magnetic field passing through it and surrounding it. The Earth has a magnetic field similar to that of an enormous bar magnet.

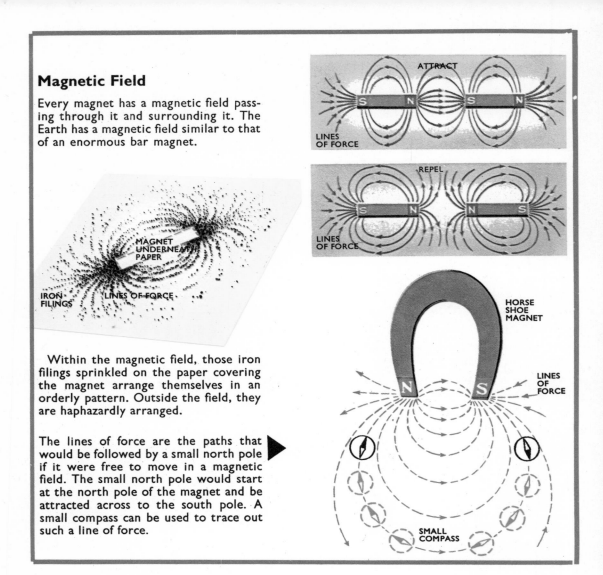

Within the magnetic field, those iron filings sprinkled on the paper covering the magnet arrange themselves in an orderly pattern. Outside the field, they are haphazardly arranged.

The lines of force are the paths that would be followed by a small north pole if it were free to move in a magnetic field. The small north pole would start at the north pole of the magnet and be attracted across to the south pole. A small compass can be used to trace out such a line of force.

TERRESTRIAL MAGNETISM

If a bar magnet is suspended in such a way that it hangs horizontally, and is set swinging in the horizontal plane, it always comes to rest pointing in the same direction. A map showing the lines of magnetic force over the surface of the Earth can be drawn by repeating this experiment at many places on the Earth. The pattern of these lines of force is very similar to that surrounding an ordinary bar magnet. On account of this and other properties which the Earth's magnetic field has in common with a magnet's,

it was concluded many years ago that the Earth is itself a magnet.

For most practical purposes the Earth may be regarded as containing a very powerful bar magnet which passes near the centre of the Earth. It would appear that the axis of this magnet is almost the same as the axis about which the Earth spins. Scientists have pointed out, however, that the temperature at the centre of the Earth is too high for iron to retain its magnetism (iron loses its magnetic properties when heated above 760°C):

there is at present no really satisfactory explanation of the source of the magnetic field around the Earth.

The pole near the end of the freely suspended bar magnet which comes to rest pointing in a northerly direction, is for obvious reasons, called the *north seeking pole* of the magnet. Likewise, the other pole is the *south seeking pole*. Since unlike magnetic poles attract one another (and like poles repel) it follows that the north seeking pole of the suspended bar magnet (or of any compass) is turned to point northwards by the *attraction*

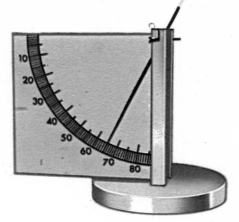

The Dip Needle is used to measure the angle between the horizontal and the lines of magnetic force at a particular place.

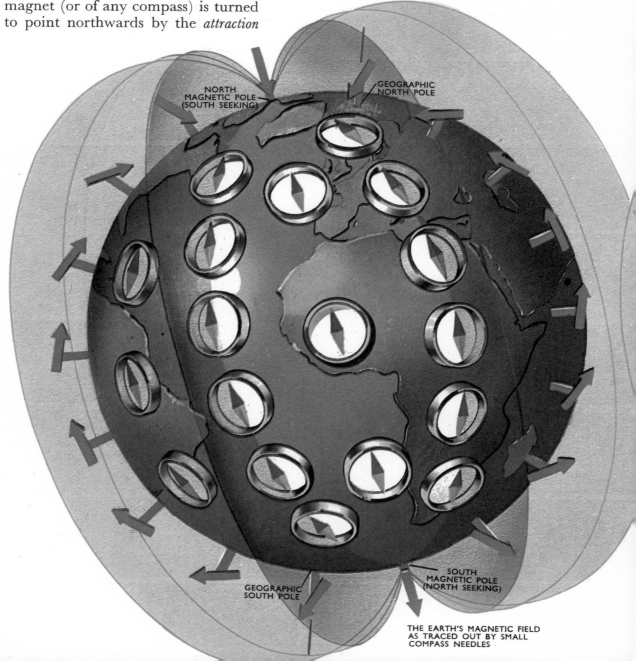

THE EARTH'S MAGNETIC FIELD
AS TRACED OUT BY SMALL
COMPASS NEEDLES

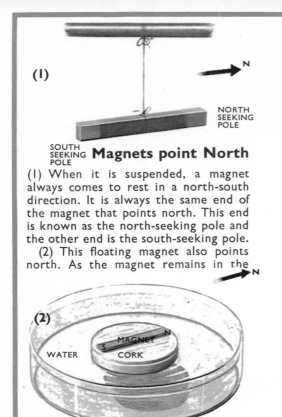

(1)

NORTH SEEKING POLE

SOUTH SEEKING POLE

Magnets point North

(1) When it is suspended, a magnet always comes to rest in a north-south direction. It is always the same end of the magnet that points north. This end is known as the north-seeking pole and the other end is the south-seeking pole.

(2) This floating magnet also points north. As the magnet remains in the

(2) WATER MAGNET N S CORK

(3)

centre of the bowl, both ends must be of equal strength. If not, the magnet would move in the direction where the attraction was the strongest.

(3) A small lightweight magnet is used in a compass. It is pivoted so that it can move freely and is protected by a non-magnetic case with a transparent top. This device works because the Earth behaves as though it has an enormous bar magnet inside it with its ends under the Poles, its south pole somewhere underneath the Earth's magnetic North Pole. This south pole attracts the north-seeking pole of the magnet.

of the Earth's south seeking pole. This *south seeking pole* is situated at the *North Magnetic Pole* of the Earth. Similarly there must be a north seeking pole at the South Magnetic Pole. The names are confusing but it is logical when you think about it.

On the magnetic map of the World, the positions of the poles may be

The shape of the Solar Corona indicates that the Sun also has a strong magnetic field.

identified as the two points on the surface of the Earth towards which the lines of magnetic force converge. From such a map it is found that the Magnetic Poles do not coincide with the Geographic Poles of the Earth. Furthermore, over the years the positions of the Magnetic Poles have changed. The present position of the North Magnetic Pole is approximately 75° 30'N, 100°W, that of the South Magnetic Pole approximately 66° 30'S, 140°E.

For the same reasons there are only a few places on the Earth's surface where the geographic meridian and the magnetic meridian are parallel to one another. The two lines usually cross one another and the angle between these two different meridians, which pass through a particular place, is called the *declination* (or magnetic variation). Not only does the declination vary from place to place, it also changes with time.

On the more accurate types of large-scale map, the magnetic variation at the date of publication is shown in the margin. The variation in London, for instance, is now about 7° 20 W, and is decreasing by about 7' each year. Failure to correct a course for such a variation could have serious consequences – at the end of a 10-mile journey in a straight line, one would be over 200 yards off course.

It is possible to make a reasonable estimate of the declination or magnetic variation using a good magnetic compass and a map of the area in which one is situated. Observations of this type are best carried out from a hillside so that a large area of country is easily visible.

One or more easily identifiable features (e.g. church, cross-roads, windmill) which are some distance from the observation station should be chosen. The compass bearing of the distant point which must also be fixed by the map is measured first.

The bearing of that point (i.e. the angle which a line drawn on the map from the observation station to the point, makes with the North-South line on the map) is also measured on the map with a protractor. The difference between these two angles is the magnetic variation.

From the diagram showing the magnetic field of the Earth it will be seen that the angle which the lines of force make with the surface of the Earth varies widely over the globe. At the North and South Magnetic Poles the lines of force are vertical, whereas at the equator they are almost horizontal. The angle between the lines of magnetic force at any point and the horizontal is known as the *angle of dip*.

Dip may be measured with a magnetized needle (*a dip-needle*) which is free to turn in a vertical plane about a horizontal pivot. The whole apparatus is placed so that the plane in which the needle turns is in the magnetic meridian.

CHAPTER TEN

Electromagnetism

Magnetism and Electricity

When an electric current is passed through a coil of wire, the coil behaves just as though it is a bar magnet. Its

CONVENTIONAL CURRENT FLOW

LINES OF FORCE

lines of force are similarly shaped. The strength of this magnetic field depends on the size of the current passing through the coil and the number of turns of wire there are in the coil.

The Left-hand Rule

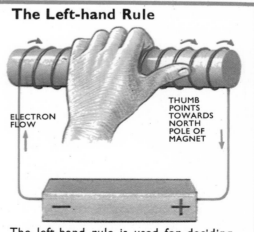

ELECTRON FLOW

THUMB POINTS TOWARDS NORTH POLE OF MAGNET

The left-hand rule is used for deciding which end of the coil is the north pole and which end is the south pole. The left hand grasps the coil so that the fingers point in the direction of the electron flow. (This is from negative to positive, *i.e.* the opposite direction to the conventional current flow.) The thumb points towards the north pole.

Electromagnets

CORE OF SOFT IRON
INSIDE COILS

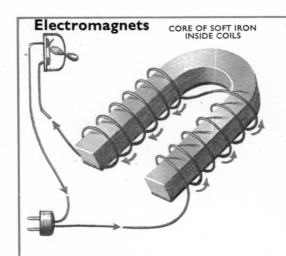

Simple Generator

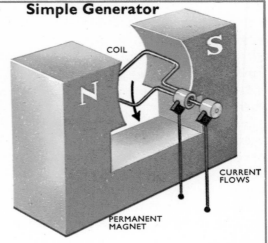

COIL

N S

CURRENT FLOWS

PERMANENT MAGNET

The strength of the magnetic field of a coil of wire is increased by putting a soft iron core inside it. The soft iron is quickly magnetised by the field passing through it. Coil and core are together known as an electromagnet. Almost as soon as the current is switched off it loses its magnetism. Electromagnets can be extremely powerful – powerful enough to lift large heaps of scrap iron and can be switched off at will. Electromagnets are used in the electric motors and generators of many pieces of electrical apparatus.

Whenever a wire is moved so that it cuts lines of force in a magnetic field a voltage is set up in the wire. If the wire is in a circuit, then as long as the lines of force are being cut, an electric current will flow round the circuit. In practice, electromagnets provide the magnetic field and many wires cut the lines of force to provide the electric current. A *motor* is the reverse of a generator. A current passed round a coil in the field of an electromagnet makes the coil rotate.

TRANSFORMERS AND WHAT THEY DO

There are always at least two circuits connected to one transformer. Alternating current is passed from one circuit to another through the transformer, but direct current is stopped. And generally the voltage (potential) of an electric signal is changed as it passes through the transformer.

A transformer in its simplest form consists of two *separate* coils of insulated wire wound round the *same* iron core. Each coil is part of a *separate* circuit. Current flows into the transformer through one coil, the *primary*, and another current, the image of the first one, flows out through the other coil, or *secondary*. When an electric current flows in a coil of wire, the coil behaves as though it were a magnet. This is an *electromagnet* effect, and both direct and alternating currents produce it. A magnet influences not only objects actually touching it, but also those near it. In other words, an electric *field* extends around the magnet. This will be a constant field if D.C. flows in the primary, and a changing field if A.C. flows.

By winding the coil on an iron ring, the field is *concentrated in the ring* (strong magnetic fields are always made with the aid of metals containing iron). The two coils are both wound on the same iron ring, and the secondary therefore lies in the field produced by the primary. The constant field produced by a direct current in the primary will not usefully affect the secondary. But the varying strength of an alternating current causes a building and collapsing magnetic field that induces a varying current to flow through the secondary (provided, of course, that the secondary circuit is completed). In fact, the secondary current is proportional to the *rate of change* of the primary current (i.e. the rate at which the magnetic field builds up and collapses). When the primary current is not changing (D.C. current), no current flows in the secondary. An alternating signal in the secondary will be very similar to the signal put into the primary. But its voltage may be larger or smaller, and its current may be smaller or larger. The reason

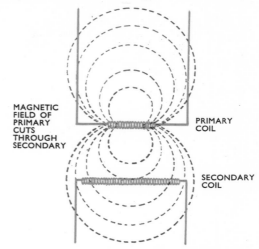

Diagram of a transformer (simplified).

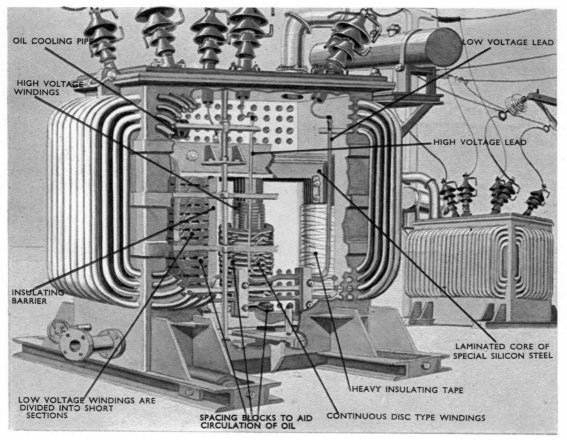

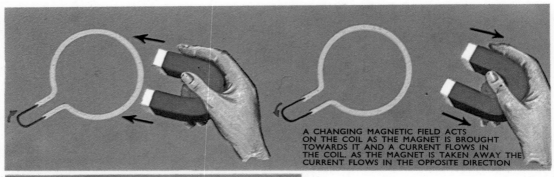

A CHANGING MAGNETIC FIELD ACTS ON THE COIL AS THE MAGNET IS BROUGHT TOWARDS IT AND A CURRENT FLOWS IN THE COIL. AS THE MAGNET IS TAKEN AWAY THE CURRENT FLOWS IN THE OPPOSITE DIRECTION

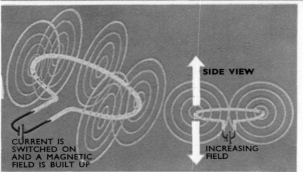

SIDE VIEW

CURRENT IS SWITCHED ON AND A MAGNETIC FIELD IS BUILT UP

INCREASING FIELD

When a to-and-fro alternating current flows in a coil it causes a rapid building-up and collapsing of a magnetic field. If a second coil is placed near the first coil, the changing magnetic field causes an alternating current to flow in the second coil.

SIDE VIEW

CURRENT IS SWITCHED OFF AND THE MAGNETIC FIELD COLLAPSES

DECREASING FIELD

CURRENT IS SWITCHED ON IN THE OPPOSITE DIRECTION

THE MAGNETIC FIELD BUILDS UP AGAIN

SIDE VIEW

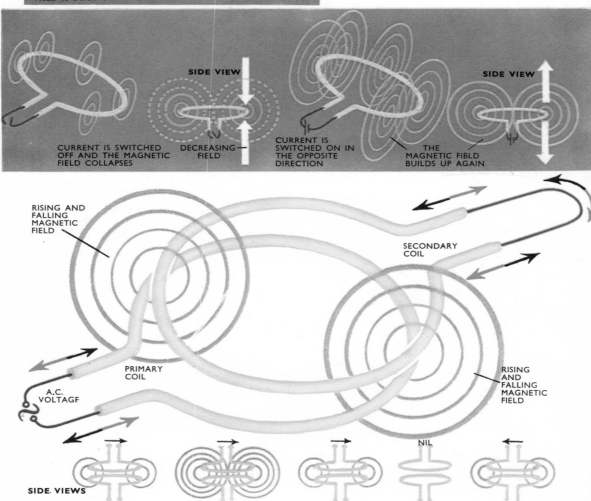

RISING AND FALLING MAGNETIC FIELD

SECONDARY COIL

PRIMARY COIL

RISING AND FALLING MAGNETIC FIELD

A.C. VOLTAGE

NIL

SIDE VIEWS

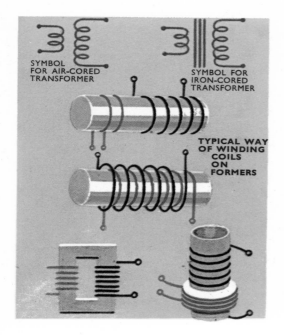

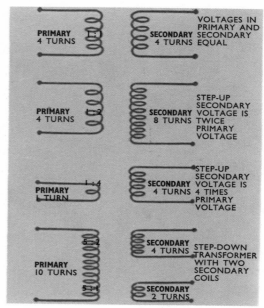

for this is that the two coils may have different numbers of turns. The voltage across each coil will be proportional to the number of turns in the coil, and, in an ideal transformer, the ratio of the voltage going into the transformer to the voltage going out is simply the ratio of the number of turns in the primary to the number in the secondary. Say there are 10 turns in the primary and 50 turns in the secondary. Then 1 volt applied across the primary coil will become 5 volts across the secondary coil.

What is more important is that *power* must be transmitted across the transformer. Electricity is usually put to work, and power is its rate of doing it. Electric power is current multiplied by voltage:

Power (in watts) = amps × volts. If there are 2 amps at 1 volt then the power is 2 watts. This is to be transferred from primary to secondary. 2 watts pass through the secondary, but this is now at 5 volts pressure. What can the current be in the secondary?

$$\text{Current} = \frac{\text{power (in watts)}}{\text{voltage}}$$

so current $= \frac{2 \text{ watts}}{5 \text{ volts}} = \frac{2}{5}$ amp.

So the maximum possible current in the secondary is only $\frac{2}{5}$ amp.

This is the principle behind its use in the electricity supply network, where transformers increase the voltage and reduce the current so that it can be transmitted without losing much energy (Energy loss through heating is I^2R, where I is the current and R is the resistance.) These are called *step-up* transformers. *Step-down* transformers decrease the voltage to a safer value at the end of the line. In the telephone the transformer steps up the signal voltage about twice, and reduces the current and resistance loss along the wires. It also divides the alternating signal from the direct current passing through the microphone. In a full-wave rectifier used in a radio detecting circuit, the secondary coil is split into two, each going to a separate diode. One primary may give power to several secondaries.

43

CHAPTER ELEVEN

Types of Magnetism

Manufacture of Permanent Magnets

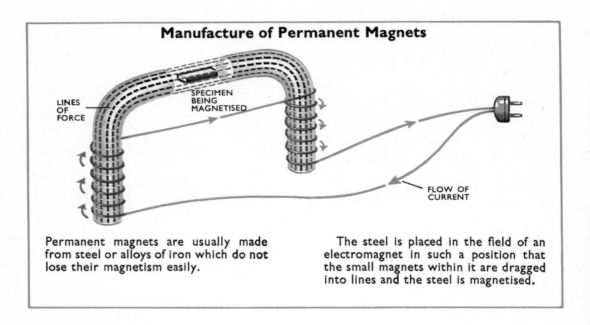

LINES OF FORCE

SPECIMEN BEING MAGNETISED

FLOW OF CURRENT

Permanent magnets are usually made from steel or alloys of iron which do not lose their magnetism easily.

The steel is placed in the field of an electromagnet in such a position that the small magnets within it are dragged into lines and the steel is magnetised.

Types of Magnetism

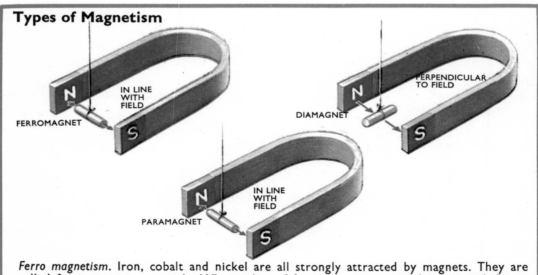

FERROMAGNET

IN LINE WITH FIELD

DIAMAGNET

PERPENDICULAR TO FIELD

PARAMAGNET

IN LINE WITH FIELD

Ferro magnetism. Iron, cobalt and nickel are all strongly attracted by magnets. They are called ferromagnetic materials. When a bar of ferromagnetic material is suspended in a magnetic field, it comes to rest with its length parallel to the magnetic field. *All* substances are magnetic to some extent. They fall into two groups, paramagnets and diamagnets. Paramagnets (which include ferromagnets) line up parallel to the magnetic field. Diamagnets come to rest with their length cutting across the lines of force, *i.e.* at 90° to the magnetic field in which they are suspended.

Coils and
Alternating Current

CHAPTER TWELVE

Electric Current — A.C. and D.C.

THE current produced by a battery is a *direct current* (D.C.) because it flows in the *same* direction all the time. The electrons drift along a metal wire in one direction from the negative terminal of the battery to the positive terminal (the 'conventional' current shown in circuit diagrams flows from positive to negative). When the direction of the flow of electricity is reversed at regular intervals the current is called an *alternating current* (A.C.) The electrons surge backwards and forwards along the wire.

Each complete to-and-fro motion of the electric current is called a *cycle*, and the number of to-and-fro motions (cycles) that the current makes in one second is called its *frequency*. In the United Kingdom the electricity used in homes is supplied at 50 cycles per second. In the United States the frequency is 60 cycles per second.

As the illustrations show, the strength (electrons flowing per second) and direction of the alternating current are changing all the time. During a complete cycle the current strength starts at zero (no electrons flowing) and builds up to a maximum flow in one direction before falling again to zero (stopping) and

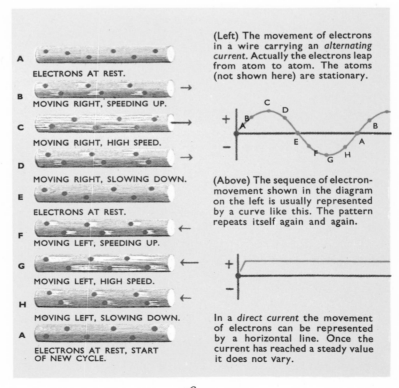

A   ELECTRONS AT REST.

B   MOVING RIGHT, SPEEDING UP.

C   MOVING RIGHT, HIGH SPEED.

D   MOVING RIGHT, SLOWING DOWN.

E   ELECTRONS AT REST.

F   MOVING LEFT, SPEEDING UP.

G   MOVING LEFT, HIGH SPEED.

H   MOVING LEFT, SLOWING DOWN.

A   ELECTRONS AT REST, START OF NEW CYCLE.

(Left) The movement of electrons in a wire carrying an *alternating current*. Actually the electrons leap from atom to atom. The atoms (not shown here) are stationary.

(Above) The sequence of electron-movement shown in the diagram on the left is usually represented by a curve like this. The pattern repeats itself again and again.

In a *direct current* the movement of electrons can be represented by a horizontal line. Once the current has reached a steady value it does not vary.

Practical Uses for Transformers

When an alternating current passes through a coil of wire it causes a fluctuating magnetic field to spread out. If this field cuts through another *quite unconnected* coil of wire nearby (i.e. a *separate* circuit) it produces a 'voltage' which actually makes an electric current flow in the second coil in *time* with the alternating current of the first. The size of the second voltage depends on the number of turns of wire in each coil. If there are 10 turns in the first coil (primary) and 100 turns in the second coil (secondary) the voltage is stepped up 10 times (i.e. $\frac{100}{10}$). A transformer in which there are more turns on the secondary coil than on the primary is called a 'step-up' transformer since it raises the voltage. If there are less turns on the secondary (e.g. 10) than on the primary (e.g. 100) then the voltage will be decreased to $\frac{10}{100}$ (i.e. $\frac{1}{10}$) of its former value. This is a 'step-down' transformer.

In practice both coils are wound round an iron core which concentrates the magnetic field. A transformer will not work with direct current because the steady flow of direct current only produces a steady magnetic field. It is the *rise and fall* in magnetic field produced by an alternating current in a coil that sets up a voltage in a separate coil nearby. To increase the voltage of a *direct* current supply it must first be changed to A.C. which is then fed into a step-up transformer. The high-voltage current obtained from the transformer later has to be "rectified" or turned back into D.C.

It might seem that when voltage is "stepped up" by a transformer the extra voltage is being obtained at no extra cost. In electricity, as in most things, we do not get something for nothing. In the case of the transformer the extra voltage is obtained at the expense of current: as the voltage is stepped up so the current is stepped down.

then starts again in the opposite direction building up to a maximum flow in the opposite direction before again coming to a stop (zero flow).

With a *direct* current from a battery the current strength increases from zero to a steady level as soon as the circuit is completed. Only when the circuit is disconnected, or when the battery runs down, does the current strength fall off.

Although the eye apparently sees a continuous output of light from an electric lamp working off the A.C. mains supply, the light is in fact flickering very rapidly – 100 times per second when the frequency of the current is 50 cycles per second (120 times per second for 60 cycles per second). This is because at two points in each cycle the current strength falls to zero (at the instant when the electrons change direction they are not flowing). Because the strength and direction of the electron flow in a direct current are constant a light supplied by direct current does not flicker.

A.C. is just as efficient as D.C. for operating electrical apparatus, such as heating appliances, lights, and motors. In addition A.C. has one remarkable advantage – it can multiply or divide its voltage (potential) with the aid of two coils of wire – a transformer.

The voltage of an alternating current can be changed much more efficiently and easily than the voltage of a direct current. For this reason the electricity supplied to our homes is nearly always in the form of an alternating current. To change the voltage of the A.C. mains a transformer is used, but this device cannot change a steady (D.C.) voltage.

It is possible to generate an alternating current of several thousand volts at the power station. With a transformer this can be stepped up to hundreds of thousands of volts for carriage in overhead supply lines. It can then be stepped down for supply to the home in hundreds of volts. If electricity were sent all the way from the power station to the consumer at a low 'pressure' of, say, 240 volts the supply lines would become hot and waste a great deal of electrical energy.

CHAPTER THIRTEEN

Alternating Power — R.M.S.

IS alternating current as good value for money as direct current? Are both as good for heating? A direct current stays at a steady value all the time, while an alternating current rises up to a peak value, drops down to zero, and starts to build up and drop down again in the opposite direction. Obviously there is more electricity in the direct current, if it has the same value as the peak of the alternating current.

This is taken into consideration when A.C. voltages are quoted, so that both A.C. and D.C. are as good as each other at heating. When the mains supply is said to be 240 volts A.C. this is only a modest estimate of the voltage, which actually rises to nearly 340 volts at the peak of the alternating cycle. But 240 volts is the *effective* voltage of the current supply. The D.C. would give exactly the same heating effect as an A.C. voltage with a peak value of about 340 volts.

The effective A.C. value is called the *root-mean-square* value. It can be calculated from the peak value by dividing the peak value by the square root of two.

Averages and Mean Squares

A root-mean-square is a complicated form of average. The simple arithmetical average (sometimes called *arithmethic mean*) of one, two, three and four is two-and-a-half. It is the sum of the numbers (ten) divided by the number of numbers (four). However, there is no point in quoting the simple

average value of the mains supply of electric current, which flows first in one direction, and then in the opposite direction. It is usual to regard the current going in one direction as positive, and in the other direction as negative, so the average current in one complete cycle is nil. The positive current is exactly equal to the negative current. There is no *net* flow of current.

It is nonsense to suggest that the net *effect* of the current is also nil. An

The electrons which make up the electric current have difficulty in drifting through an electrical resistance wire (such as the heating element of an electric fire). As a result of their collisions with atoms in the resistance wire, the electrons lose some of their energy. The energy is radiated away from the wire as heat energy. The heating effect is proportional to the resistance. It does not matter whether the current is one-way (diagram on the left) or to-and-fro (diagrams at the centre and right) – the electron current still encounters resistance, and there is a heating effect. R.M.S. alternating current has the same heating effect as a direct current of the same voltage.

HEAT RADIATED

DIRECT CURR

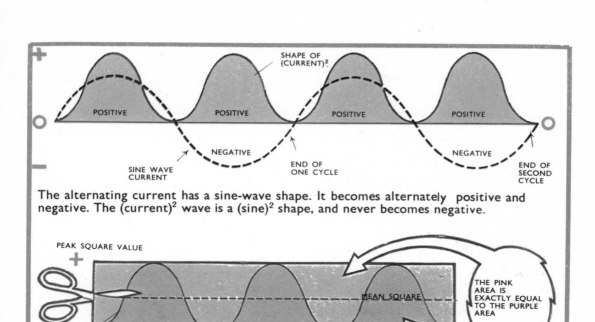

The alternating current has a sine-wave shape. It becomes alternately positive and negative. The (current)^2 wave is a (sine)^2 shape, and never becomes negative.

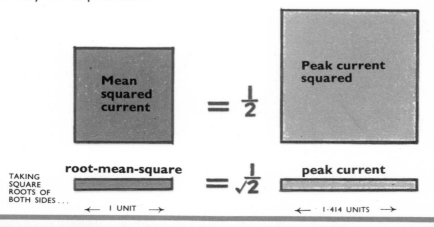

What is the average squared current? The heating effect depends on the square of the current, so the average (or mean) squared current is obviously the value needed to quote as an effective current. The curve above is symmetrical. Its average value is exactly half its peak value.

Mean squared current $= \dfrac{1}{2}$ Peak current squared

TAKING SQUARE ROOTS OF BOTH SIDES...

root-mean-square $= \dfrac{1}{\sqrt{2}}$ peak current

$\leftarrow$ 1 UNIT $\rightarrow$

$\leftarrow$ 1·414 UNITS $\rightarrow$

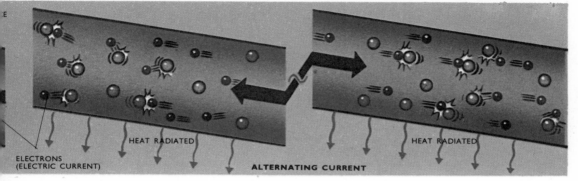

ELECTRONS (ELECTRIC CURRENT)

HEAT RADIATED

HEAT RADIATED

ALTERNATING CURRENT

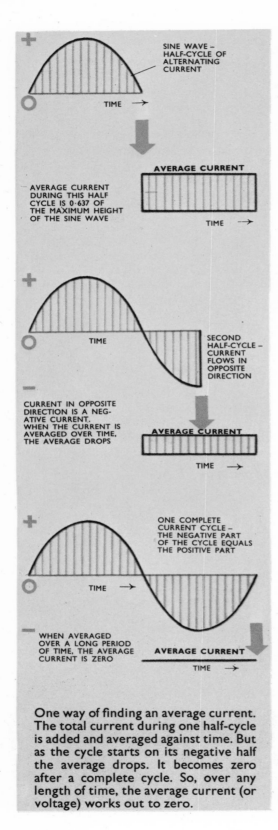

Within the figure, the following labels appear:

SINE WAVE – HALF-CYCLE OF ALTERNATING CURRENT

TIME →

AVERAGE CURRENT

TIME →

AVERAGE CURRENT DURING THIS HALF CYCLE IS 0·637 OF THE MAXIMUM HEIGHT OF THE SINE WAVE

TIME

SECOND HALF-CYCLE – CURRENT FLOWS IN OPPOSITE DIRECTION

CURRENT IN OPPOSITE DIRECTION IS A NEGATIVE CURRENT. WHEN THE CURRENT IS AVERAGED OVER TIME, THE AVERAGE DROPS

AVERAGE CURRENT

TIME →

ONE COMPLETE CURRENT CYCLE – THE NEGATIVE PART OF THE CYCLE EQUALS THE POSITIVE PART

TIME →

WHEN AVERAGED OVER A LONG PERIOD OF TIME, THE AVERAGE CURRENT IS ZERO

AVERAGE CURRENT

TIME →

One way of finding an average current. The total current during one half-cycle is added and averaged against time. But as the cycle starts on its negative half the average drops. It becomes zero after a complete cycle. So, over any length of time, the average current (or voltage) works out to zero.

Averages and Mean Squares

The arithmetical average of 1, 2, 3 and 4 is 2·5. The root-mean-square of these same numbers is the square root of the average square, and works out to be about 2·74. The squares are 1, 4, 9 and 16 – total – 30. The average square is 30 divided by 4 (4 is the number of numbers), or 7·5. The root-mean-square is therefore slightly greater than the arithmetical average in this example.

electric fire plugged in to the mains soon heats up as alternating current flows first in one direction and then in the other direction through the heating element. The heating effect depends on the square of the current (the current multiplied by itself, written as (current)^2). Whether the current is positive or negative, the *square is always positive*. So the effective current is based on the (current)^2. This can never cancel out to nothing.

To find the root-mean-square, the current at each instant is multiplied by itself. A graph of current against time shows the 'shape' of the current waveform. It is a smooth curve, a *sine-wave*, oscillating up and down. The graph of current-squared (current)^2 is also a smooth curve, but it has a different shape, and it never drops below the zero line. The square of the current is always positive, so it has an average, or *mean square* value. It is awkward to leave it as a squared current, so the square root of the mean square is found. This is why the effective current is called the root-mean-square.

At first sight, it looks as though formidable mathematics are needed to work out the relationship between the root-mean-square value and the peak

50

value. The shape of the current-squared graph is a continuously-changing curve. It would be most convenient if the mean square current were exactly half the peak square current. It turns out, rather surprisingly, to be just this.

If the area under the current-squared curve is shaded in, then it can be seen that the unshaded parts in between the shaded parts are of exactly the same size, shape and area. The shaded parts cover half of the area topped by the line drawn through the current-squared peaks. So the mean square current is also half of the peak value.

$$\text{mean-square current} = \frac{(\text{peak current})^2}{2}$$

The root-mean-square is calculated by finding the square roots of both sides of this equation.

$$\text{root-mean-square current} = \frac{\text{peak current}}{2}$$

The square root of 2 is 1·414. The peak current divided by 1·414 is the same as the peak current multiplied by 0·707.

D.C.

SAME HEATING EFFECT

240 VOLTS D.C.

A current at 240 volts D.C. would give the same heating effect as a current at 240 volts A.C. This is because the to-and-fro nature of the current has been taken into account when the A.C. voltage is counted. 240 volts is only about seven-tenths of the maximum alternating voltage. It is the root-mean square (R.M.S.,) value

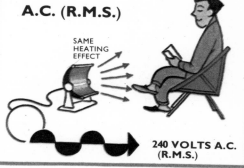

A.C. (R.M.S.)

SAME HEATING EFFECT

240 VOLTS A.C. (R.M.S.)

CHAPTER FOURTEEN

Chokes and Inductive Reactance

SWITCH a battery across a re-sistance, and the current in the circuit immediately jumps to its full value (which depends of course on the electrical potential supplied by the battery and the resistance in the circuit according to Ohm's law). But replace the resistance with a *choke* (a large coil of wire), and the current rises *gradually* to its full value, again determined by the resistance of the coil (all wires have a certain amount of electrical resistance). Some pro-perty of the coil resists the *change* in current. This property is called *induc-tance*, and the 'resistance' the coil offers to changing currents is called *inductive reactance*.

When a current flows through a wire it sets up a magnetic field around the wire. As the current rises or falls,

the magnetic field rises or collapses, *i.e.* it is a *moving* field. When the wire is coiled into a series of loops the magnetic field around one loop cuts some of the other loops. Whenever *moving* magnetic fields cut wires, they generate a difference in electric po-tential (i.e. an electromotive force or e.m.f.) which pushes a *current* through the wires, provided the current has a complete circuit to flow around. This is one of the two fundamental principles of electro-magnetism – the generator principle. In the electric generator a moving coil rotates through a steady magnetic field and makes a current flow in the wire. A steady field on a moving coil has the same effect as a moving field on a steady coil the – generation of a *current*.

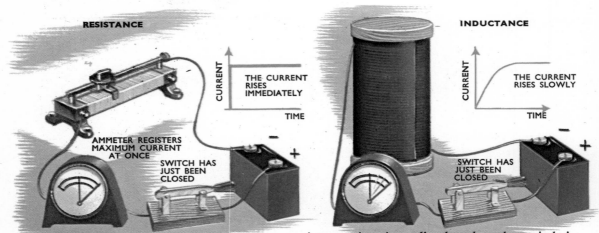

A direct current connected across a resistance rises immediately when the switch is closed. But the current through an inductance rises slowly. Whenever the current in a coil of wire changes, a current is generated in the opposite direction, if it has a complete circuit to flow around.

So as soon as a current starts to flow round the coil, it makes a growing magnetic field, which generates another separate current. The generated current could flow in either of two directions, either in the same direction as the current from the battery, or in the opposite direction. If it flowed in the same direction, it would increase the field around the coil, which would generate a bigger current in the adjacent coils, and the process would repeat itself, the current rapidly increasing without limit.

But this is not what we see when the battery is switched across the coil. In fact, the current slowly builds up to a steady maximum. So the current must flow in the opposite direction, and tends to *reduce* the *total* current in the coil. The backwards current is never as large as the forwards current from the battery, which must win in the end. As the current approaches its maximum value, it changes more slowly and the back e.m.f. and the backwards current are therefore smaller. When the magnetic field is steady there is no backwards current at all.

The more turns of wire there are in the coil the more turns each turn can affect, or the greater the coil's *inductance*. Its *inductive reactance*, the resistance - to - change it offers, is greater.

Inductance affects a D.C. circuit only when the current is switched on and switched off. Alternating current, on the other hand, is changing its direction, to-and-fro, all the time. The more rapidly the current changes, the more rapidly the magnetic field it makes changes, and the greater will be the inductive reactance which tries to slow down the change.

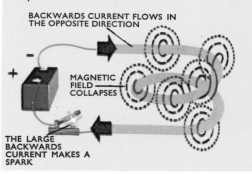

A collapsing magnetic field generates a current in the opposite direction, and a spark across the switch.

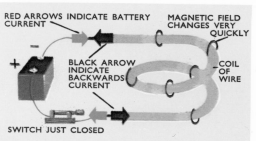

The back E.M.F. and the backwards current in the coil is greatest when the current supply is just switched on.

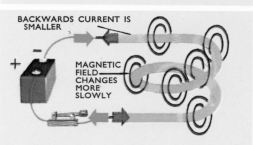

An instant later. As the magnetic field changes more slowly, the backwards current is smaller.

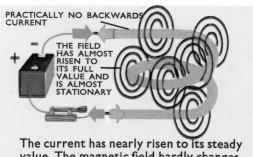

The current has nearly risen to its steady value. The magnetic field hardly changes, so there is very little backwards current.

CHAPTER FIFTEEN

Current Lag and Lead

A CURRENT flowing around an electric circuit may meet with three different kinds of opposition, or *impedance*. They are caused by resistance (R), inductance (L) and capacitance (C).

Of these, resistance is the easiest to understand, because it has the same effect on both direct, steady, currents and on alternating, to-and-fro, currents. When the electrical potential difference, or voltage, across the two terminals of a resistance changes, the current changes immediately. If the voltage rises, the current rises; and if the voltage falls, the current falls, and so on. Current and voltage are said to be *in phase*.

Inductors (L) and capacitors (C) behave quite differently. In 'L' circuits a rise in voltage is accompanied by a rise in current, but this rise is delayed by a back e.m.f. generated in the inductor. As the voltage rises and falls, the current rises and falls, but *a fraction of a second later*. So the current flowing through the inductor is always lagging behind the voltage, and current and voltage are said to be *out of phase*.

In 'C' circuits, on the other hand, the current in the circuit must first flow to the two plates of the capacitor ('round' the circuit from plate to plate and *not* across the gap between the plates) to make a voltage difference across them. As the current rises, the voltage between the two plates rises; and as the current falls, the voltage falls, but *the voltage follows the current's lead a fraction of a second later*. Current and voltage are again out of phase, only in 'C' circuits the current is always leading the voltage.

One complete cycle of an alternating current consists of a rise (in current or voltage) up to the positive maximum, followed by a drop, through zero, to the negative maximum voltage, and a subsequent rise back to the zero starting point. A

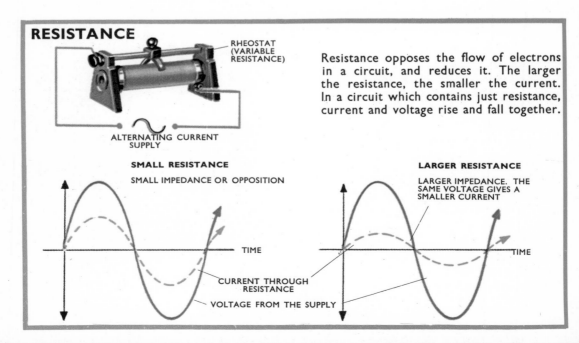

RESISTANCE

RHEOSTAT (VARIABLE RESISTANCE)

ALTERNATING CURRENT SUPPLY

Resistance opposes the flow of electrons in a circuit, and reduces it. The larger the resistance, the smaller the current. In a circuit which contains just resistance, current and voltage rise and fall together.

SMALL RESISTANCE

SMALL IMPEDANCE OR OPPOSITION

LARGER RESISTANCE

LARGER IMPEDANCE. THE SAME VOLTAGE GIVES A SMALLER CURRENT

TIME

TIME

CURRENT THROUGH RESISTANCE

VOLTAGE FROM THE SUPPLY

In an inductor, the current has to wait before it can flow until the force trying to push it through (the supply voltage) is greater than the force trying to push it back in the opposite direction (the back e.m.f.). So the current lags behind the voltage.

A changing current in a coil makes a changing magnetic field around it. At the start of the alternating current cycle the voltage across the coil increases quickly as it tries to send a current through the coil. But as soon as the current starts to go through the coil, it makes a rapidly changing magnetic field which results in a force (called an electromotive force, or e.m.f. for short), pushing another current of electrons back in the opposite direction. At the start of the cycle the voltage from the supply changes so quickly that it generates a large back e.m.f. So there is a net back e.m.f. and a backwards current. As the supply voltage approaches its maximum, it increases more slowly and the backwards current ceases to flow. The net current in the coil reaches zero a quarter of a cycle later than the voltage.

INDUCTANCE

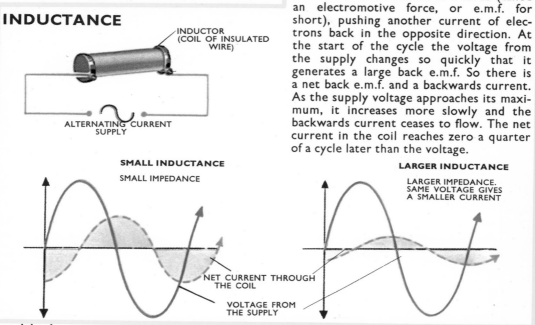

INDUCTOR (COIL OF INSULATED WIRE)

ALTERNATING CURRENT SUPPLY

SMALL INDUCTANCE

SMALL IMPEDANCE

LARGER INDUCTANCE

LARGER IMPEDANCE. SAME VOLTAGE GIVES A SMALLER CURRENT

NET CURRENT THROUGH THE COIL

VOLTAGE FROM THE SUPPLY

'positive' current means that electrons flow in one direction round the circuit, while a 'negative' current means that they surge round in the opposite direction.

In a circuit containing *only resistance*, the positive surges of current and the positive increases in voltage coincide. But in a circuit containing *only*

CAPACITANCE

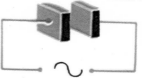

CAPACITOR (PAIR OF CONDUCTING METAL PLATES)

ALTERNATING CURRENT SUPPLY

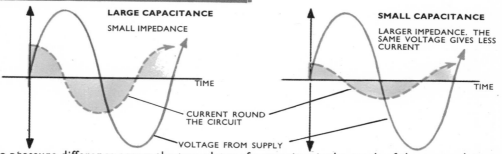

LARGE CAPACITANCE

SMALL IMPEDANCE

SMALL CAPACITANCE

LARGER IMPEDANCE. THE SAME VOLTAGE GIVES LESS CURRENT

TIME

TIME

CURRENT ROUND THE CIRCUIT

VOLTAGE FROM SUPPLY

The pressure difference across the two plates of a capacitor is the result of the accumulation of electrons (negative charges) on one plate and the lack of electrons (positive charges) on the other plate. At the start of the cycle (the plates are initially uncharged) the increasing voltage from the supply sends the maximum amount of current round the circuit to be stored on the plates. As the plates become more full of charge, it is more difficult to add more charge, and the current (flow of charge) decreases. When the voltage is at its maximum a quarter of a cycle later than the current's maximum no more charge is being added to the plates, and so the current in the circuit is zero. The current *leads* the voltage by a quarter of a cycle.

capacitance the surges of current occur a quarter of a cycle *before* the increase of voltage across the capacitance. In a circuit containing *only inductance* the current surges occur a quarter of a cycle *later*.

Suppose a capacitor and an inductor are both connected across an alternating voltage supply (i.e. connected in parallel), then the *same* voltage sends a current through each. But in the 'C' part of the circuit the current *leads* the voltage and in the 'L' part the current lags behind the voltage. If the values of inductance and capacitance are selected so that both offer the same impedance at the frequency of the alternating current supply, then the current through both 'L' and 'C' parts will be equal. But since one is a quarter of a cycle behind the voltage, and the other is a quarter of a cycle in front of the voltage, there is a difference of *phase* of a half cycle between the currents in the 'L' and 'C' parts. As one current is positive, the other current is negative (i.e. flowing in the opposite direction) and the same size as the positive current. So the two currents cancel each other out, and as a result no current flows out of the 'L' and 'C' combination, although there is an electrical potential (voltage) drop across the pair of them. So the inductor-capacitor pair offer a very large opposition or impedance to electric current, far larger than their separate impedances.

This arrangement is called a parallel tuned circuit or *rejector* circuit, because it will not allow through current of a particular frequency, the frequency at which the impedance of the capacitor is equal to the impedance of the inductor. Then the currents flowing through both parts are equal and opposite in direction. At any other frequency the two impedances will not be quite equal, the two currents will not quite cancel each other out, and some current will be able to flow right round the circuit.

A PARALLEL TUNED CIRCUIT

THE CAPACITOR AND INDUCTOR ARE CONNECTED ACROSS THE SAME ALTERNATING SUPPLY. WHEN THE CIRCUIT IS 'TUNED' SO THAT BOTH OFFER THE SAME IMPEDANCE, THE CURRENT THROUGH ONE IS MINUS THE CURRENT THROUGH THE OTHER AND NO CURRENT FLOWS OUT OF THE CIRCUIT

In a capacitor the voltage across the plates is caused by the flow of electrons from one plate to another *via the circuit*. The current must flow first to create the voltage, so it leads the voltage.

PARALLEL TUNED CIRCUIT

THE NET CURRENT IS ZERO

CURRENT THROUGH CAPACITOR PART OF CIRCUIT

CURRENT THROUGH COIL

UN-TUNED CIRCUIT

THE TWO CURRENTS DO NOT CANCEL, SO SOME CURRENT FLOWS

In a parallel tuned circuit the inductor's lag and the capacitor's lead cancel each other out, so that no net current flows out of the circuit.

Measuring Electricity

CHAPTER SIXTEEN

Measuring Currents and Voltages

A COIL of wire becomes a magnet when a current flows through the wire. If a coil like this is pivoted in a magnetic field, it will turn so that its north pole faces the south pole of the magnet.

One type of meter for measuring current or voltage depends on this movement of a coil in a magnetic field – these instruments are *moving coil meters*.

The movement of the coil is controlled by springs which also lead the current to and from it. Without springs, even the slightest current would cause the coil to turn through a right angle. The deflection of the spring-controlled coil depends on the size of the current flowing through it. It also depends on the strength of the magnet and on the size and number of turns on the coil. These factors are all constant and fixed by the manufacturer. The addition of a fixed soft iron core helps to produce a uniform magnetic field which ensures that the deflection of the coil is proportional to the current passing through it.

This instrument, called a *galvanometer* is very delicate and only a very

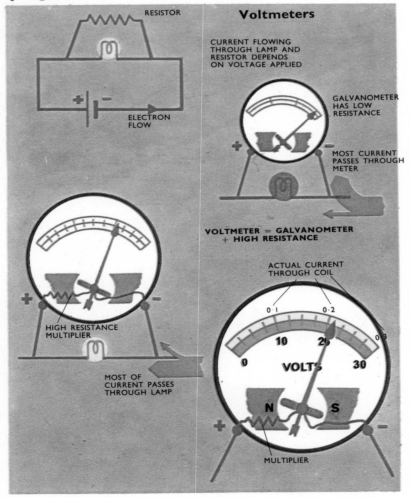

RESISTOR

ELECTRON FLOW

Voltmeters

CURRENT FLOWING THROUGH LAMP AND RESISTOR DEPENDS ON VOLTAGE APPLIED

GALVANOMETER HAS LOW RESISTANCE

MOST CURRENT PASSES THROUGH METER

VOLTMETER = GALVANOMETER + HIGH RESISTANCE

HIGH RESISTANCE MULTIPLIER

MOST OF CURRENT PASSES THROUGH LAMP

ACTUAL CURRENT THROUGH COIL

10   20   30   0

0·1   0·2   0·3

0

VOLTS

N   S

MULTIPLIER

A galvanometer is converted into a voltmeter by connecting it in series with a large resistance multiplier. The dial can then be calibrated to read volts, the voltage range depending on the resistance of the multiplier.

small current (often less than $\frac{1}{100}$ amp) can be allowed to pass through it.

Voltmeters

From Ohm's law we know that the current flowing through a resistor and lamp wired in parallel depends on the voltage drop across them.

If the voltage across the resistor and lamp is increased, the current through both is increased.

The division of the main current between lamp and resistor depends on the resistance of each. If the resistor has a low resistance like a galvanometer, current will more readily pass through it than through the lamp which may hardly glow at all.

If the resistor has a very high resistance, hardly any current will flow through it and the lamp will glow brightly.

A very high resistance (called a *multiplier*) is added to the galvanometer in series with the coil to ensure that a very small fraction of the current flows through it. This arrangement can be used as a *voltmeter*.

Using Ohm's Law it can be seen that if a higher voltage is applied, more current flows through the voltmeter (and through the lamp) and the deflection of the coil is greater.

If a voltage of 10 volts is to be measured and the resistance of the multiplier and galvanometer is 1,000 ohms, the current through the coil will be 0·01 amp $\left(I = \dfrac{V}{R} \right)$.

If the voltage is doubled the current through the coil will be 0·02 amp and the deflection is doubled. Therefore a current of 0·01 amp through the coil represents a voltage of 10 volts, 0·02 amp a voltage of 20 volts.

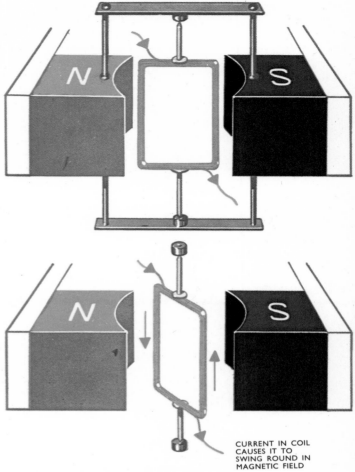

CURRENT IN COIL CAUSES IT TO SWING ROUND IN MAGNETIC FIELD

The moving-coil galvanometer. This delicate current-measuring instrument depends on movement of a coil suspended in a magnetic field when a current is passed through the coil.

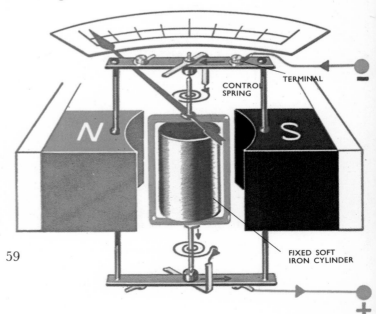

CONTROL SPRING

TERMINAL

FIXED SOFT IRON CYLINDER

59

CHAPTER SEVENTEEN

The Ammeter

THE ammeter is an instrument which measures an electric current. The units it uses are amperes (amps.), named after the famous French physicist André-Marie Ampère. There are a number of different types of ammeters but all have something in common; they contain a device called a *shunt* which allows only a very small, definite proportion of the current flowing through the circuit to pass through the measuring coil. The shunt consists simply of a wire offering the current an alternative route by-passing the instrument. But the measuring coil offers a much higher resistance to the flow of electricity through it than does

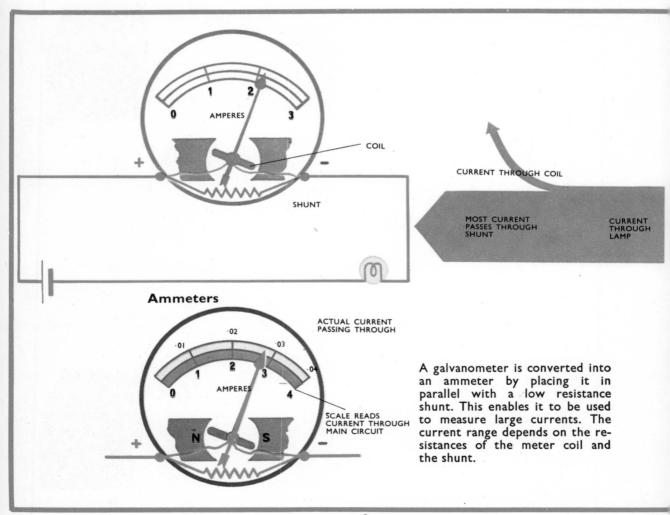

COIL

SHUNT

CURRENT THROUGH COIL

MOST CURRENT PASSES THROUGH SHUNT

CURRENT THROUGH LAMP

Ammeters

AMPERES

ACTUAL CURRENT PASSING THROUGH

SCALE READS CURRENT THROUGH MAIN CIRCUIT

A galvanometer is converted into an ammeter by placing it in parallel with a low resistance shunt. This enables it to be used to measure large currents. The current range depends on the resistances of the meter coil and the shunt.

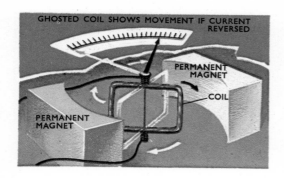

Simplified diagram illustrating the principle of the moving coil ammeter.

A very sensitive moving coil ammeter.

the shunt. Hence, most of the current takes the route of least resistance and by-passes the measuring coil.

The *moving coil* ammeter works on exactly the same principle as the galvanometer already described. It contains a pivoted coil of wire placed in the magnetic field of a permanent magnet. A magnetic field will exert a force on any wire carrying a current. Thus, the magnetic field of the permanent magnet will exert a force on the coil when a current passes through the latter and the arrangement is such that the pivoted coil is deflected, or turned. The movement of the coil is controlled by springs which also serve to lead the current to and from it.

The ammeter is able to measure an electric current because the force acting upon the coil, and hence the amount it moves, is governed by the current flowing through it.

Attached to the coil and moving with it is a pointer. This indicates on a graduated dial the current, in amperes, flowing through the coil. The fact that only a small proportion of the total circuit current flows

through the measuring coil does not matter, for it is always a definite known fraction and thus the dial can be marked so that the reading gives the total circuit current.

For example if the shunt is designed to allow $\frac{99}{100}$ of the current in the main circuit to pass through it then $\frac{1}{100}$ of the main current will pass through the coil and cause a deflection.

If the current in the circuit is 2 amps, the deflection will be produced by $\frac{2}{100}$ amp (0·02 amp). If the current flowing through the coil is half this value (0·01 amp) the current in the main circuit will be 1 amp. The scale can therefore be calibrated to read the current flowing through the main circuit.

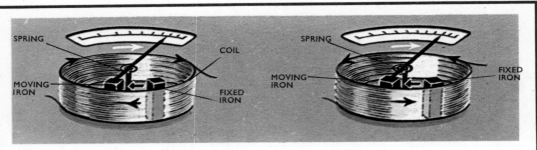

The Moving Iron Ammeter

Another ammeter, which can be used for both direct current and alternating current is the *moving iron* type. This, like the type already described, contains a measuring coil through which a small current flows producing a magnetic field. But in this case the coil is fixed, there is no permanent magnet to deflect it. Instead a movable iron vane against the opposing force of a spring is attracted into the coil when the passage of an electric current causes the latter to behave as a magnet. The principle upon which this type of ammeter works is that the amount of movement of the iron vane depends upon the strength of the magnetic field of the coil and this in turn is governed by the current flowing through it. A pointer attached to the vane indicates on a graduated dial the current flowing through the coil in amperes.

A more common type of moving iron ammeter (illustrated) contains a coil in which is a fixed block of iron and another block of iron attached to a movable pointer. The arrangement is such that when an electric current passes through the coil, both pieces of iron become magnets and repel each other no matter which way the current flows. A spring is used to restrain the moving piece of iron. The amount of repulsion, and hence the amount of movement of the pointer, depends upon the current flowing through the coil.

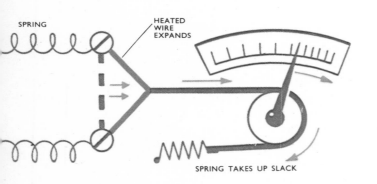

Diagram illustrating the principle of the hot wire ammeter.

A simple ammeter which works very well with a high frequency alternating current is the hot wire type. In this case the heating effect of an electric current passing through a wire causes the latter to expand and the amount of expansion depends upon the strength of the current. Since the measuring wire is always kept taut by another wire attached to a spring the second wire moves as the measuring wire expands. This movement causes a pointer to move across a dial and indicates in amperes the current flowing through the measuring wire.

CHAPTER EIGHTEEN

Paying for Electricity

PRACTICALLY every home has a variety of appliances ranging from washing machines to power tools which make use of the electrical energy supplied by generators in a power station. Since electrical energy costs money to produce and distribute, it is obvious that each consumer must pay for what he uses – hence the electricity meter which is installed in every home with an electrical supply.

An electric current is a flow of electrons through a conductor. In many ways it is like a flow of water through a pipe. Just as there must be a difference of pressure between the ends of a pipe to make water move, so there must be a voltage (a difference of 'electrical potential') between the ends of a wire to make electrons move. Batteries and generators providing the necessary voltage can be thought of as taking the place of the pumps in a water system. The rate of flow of water might be measured in gallons per second. The corresponding rate of flow of electrons (i.e. the current strength) is measured in units called amperes (usually abbreviated to amps).

Paying for electricity, however, is rather different from paying for water. Water can be paid for according to the number of gallons used. *But with electricity we are buying energy, not electrons.* The filament of a lamp contains no more electrons when it is working than when it is switched off.

From the way in which a volt (the unit in which differences of 'electrical potential' are measured) is defined, it follows that electrical power is equal to the product of the current strength and the voltage. In other words: *power in watts = current in amps multiplied by voltage.* Thus a lamp which took a current of $\frac{1}{4}$ amp from a 240-volt supply would be rated at 60 watts, since 60 watts = 240 volts × $\frac{1}{4}$ amp. 1,000 watts are called a kilowatt.

But electrical power (wattage) is the *rate* at which energy is consumed. To arrive at the actual quantity of energy used the power in watts has to be multiplied by the length of time it is being used up. The practical unit of electrical energy is the *kilowatt-hour*. Sometimes this is just called a 'unit'.

An electric kettle rated at 1,000 watts consumes one 'unit' of electrical energy every hour. An electric fire rated at 2,000 watts consumes two 'units' every hour, or one 'unit' every half-hour. A 60-watt lamp consumes one 'unit' in about seventeen hours $\left(60 \text{ watts} = \dfrac{60}{1,000} \text{ kilo-}\right.$ watts. $\dfrac{60}{1,000}$ kilowatts × 17 hours = 1·02 kilowatt-hours, or just over one 'unit').

To compute the cost of running an appliance, the number of kilowatt-hours of energy consumed is simply multiplied by the price of one 'unit'. The easiest way of computing the cost is to use one of the following formulae:

cost = power in kilowatts × time in hours × price per unit

or

$$\text{cost} = \frac{\text{power in watts}}{1,000} \times \text{time in hours} \times \text{price per unit}$$

or

$$\text{cost} = \frac{\text{amps} \times \text{volts}}{1,000} \times \text{time in hours} \times \text{price per unit.}$$

The electricity meter (its real name is the watt-hour meter) is a kind of electric motor whose speed is pro-portional to the *power* drawn from the mains. It usually has a horizontal disc which can be seen rotating – slowly when only a few appliances are switched on and quickly when many appliances are operating. The rotating disc is geared to a series of pointers moving over dials to record the number of 'units' that have been consumed.

The meter contains an electromagnet between whose poles the disc spins (diagram below illustration). When an alternating current flows through the electromagnet windings its changing field causes currents to be set up in the disc. These currents themselves have a magnetic field which repels that of the electromagnet. The force of the repulsion makes the disc rotate.

A watt-hour meter for use on A.C. It is cut away to show the rotating disc geared to a series of pointers.

ELECTRO-MAGNET

ROTATING DISC

Electric Generators
and Motors

CHAPTER NINETEEN

The Making of Electricity

ELECTRICITY is one of the most useful forms of energy because it can be delivered quickly and with little loss at the end of a cable. If an electrical 'potential' is put between the two ends of the wire there will be a steady drift of electrons jumping from atom to atom along the wire. This potential is made by ensuring that the atoms at one end of the wire are short of electrons (so they are positively charged) and those at the other end of the wire have a surplus of electrons (so they are negatively charged).

The machines in the power station which are responsible for producing electricity are called generators.

The principle of the generator is remarkably simple and quite astonishing: every time a wire is moved near the end of a magnet an electrical potential (voltage) is set up along the wire. This remarkable ability of the power of magnetism to cause a flow of electrons is still one of the mysteries of the universe. We just have to accept that there *is* a difference of electrical potential between the ends of a wire which moves in a magnetic field, and that a current of electricity will flow through any circuit connecting the ends of the wire.

A magnetic field is the name given to the region around a magnet in which its effects can be felt. In the diagrams on these pages, magnetic fields are represented by lines running from the north pole (N) of a magnet to a south pole (S). They are known as magnetic lines of force and show the direction in which the magnetic

A simple generator. On the right the coil is seen from the end making one complete revolution. The size of the current in each of the eight stages varies as shown by the curve. At stage 'e' (coil vertical) the current reverses.

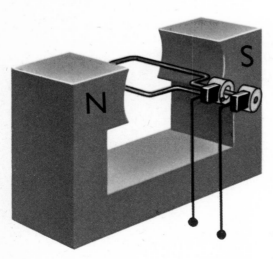
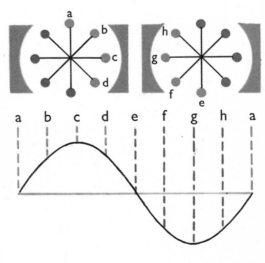

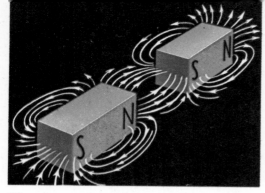

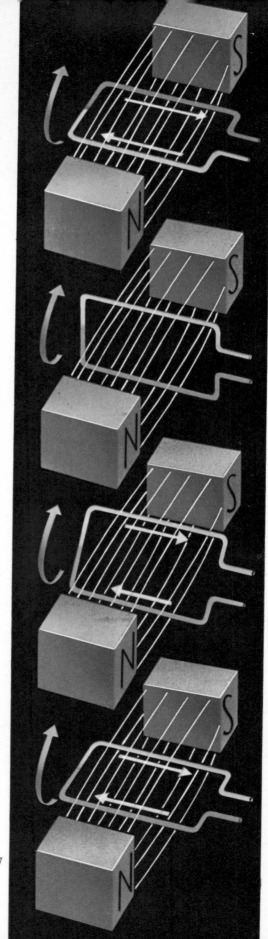

The picture above shows the magnetic field, represented by lines of force, that exists around a bar magnet. By placing two magnets with opposite poles facing, a strong and uniform field is obtained. The top picture (right) shows a single coil of wire placed in the magnetic field. As the coil is turned it cuts across the lines of force and (if it forms a part of a complete circuit) a current is produced. When the coil is in the position shown in the next picture it is moving along the lines of force without cutting them. No current is produced here. In the last two pictures the red side of the coil again cuts lines of force but this time it is moving upwards, *so the direction of the current is reversed.*

field acts at any point. A wire moving through a magnetic field so that it cuts lines of force has a voltage set up in it. When the wire is moved in the opposite direction the voltage is reversed. There is no voltage unless the wire is moving. The size of the voltage depends on the *rate* at which lines of force are cut. Consequently the faster the wire moves the greater is the voltage produced. The voltage can also be increased by using a longer piece of wire, provided that the whole of the wire cuts lines of force. That is why a compact coil of many turns of wire is preferable to a single straight wire. But a coil takes up more space and so it is necessary to have a concentrated magnetic field. Two magnets arranged with unlike poles (a north and a south) facing each other produce

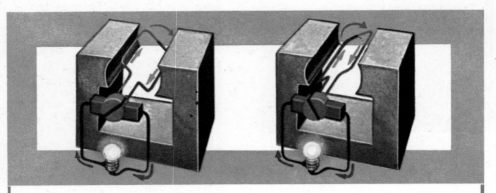

Direct Current A generator can be made to give a 'one-way' or direct current by connecting the ends of the coil to the two halves of a 'split ring' that replaces the brass collars. This device neatly puts whatever is the 'outgoing' end of the coil onto the same brush at the moment the coil comes up to the vertical and reverses the flow. In the first of the diagrams above, the red side of the coil is moving downwards and the current produced in it flows *out of* the coil into the right hand brush. In the second diagram the red side of the coil is moving upwards and now the current produced in it flows *into* the coil. But by this time the red side of the coil is connected to the left hand brush. So the current still flows out of the right hand brush, through the lamp and re-enters the generator at the left hand brush as it did in the previous diagram.

The 'split ring' route-changing switch is called a commutator. Although the commutator ensures that the current always flows in the same direction, it does not prevent the current from falling to zero each time the coil reaches the vertical position. No current is produced when the coil is vertical because it moves along the lines of force instead of cutting across them. With a number of coils it is possible to have the current in one reaching maximum value when the current in another is zero. The commutator in that case consists of several pairs of segments arranged around the axle instead of the two halves of the split ring. The segments are insulated from each other, and the ends of each coil are connected to opposite segments.

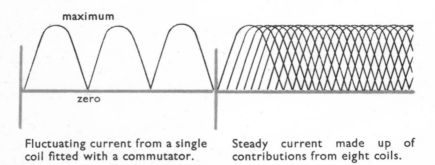

Fluctuating current from a single coil fitted with a commutator.

Steady current made up of contributions from eight coils.

a field between them in which the lines of force are straighter and more concentrated than the spread of lines around a single magnet. The easiest way to make the wire in the coil cut lines of force is to rotate it between magnets, so that each time it turns both sides of the coil are cutting right

through most of the lines of force.

The current produced by rotating a coil of wire between magnets is not steady. It is greatest when the coil lies parallel to the lines of force since this is the position where the coil cuts straight across the lines of force. No current is produced when the coil lies

68

at right angles to the lines of force because in this position the coil is moving along the lines of force and not across them. Following one side of the coil as it rotates we see that for almost half of each revolution it moves upwards through the lines of force but for most of the other half of the revolution it is moving downwards. As a result the current changes its direction twice in each revolution of the coil. It is, in fact, an alternating (to and fro) current just like the alternating current (A.C.) of the household mains supply. Sometimes one-way or direct current (D.C.) is required. One method of producing it is explained on the opposite page.

A practical generator has several coils placed like the spokes of a wheel. They are wound on an iron core which helps to concentrate the magnetic lines of force which they cut.

The magnets to make the lines of force are not ordinary iron bar magnets. They are, in fact, a pair of

A PRACTICAL GENERATOR. In this diagram the iron core that fills the space between the axle and the rotating coils has been removed for clarity. The magnetic field is provided by the two electro-magnet coils ('field windings') which also have iron cores.

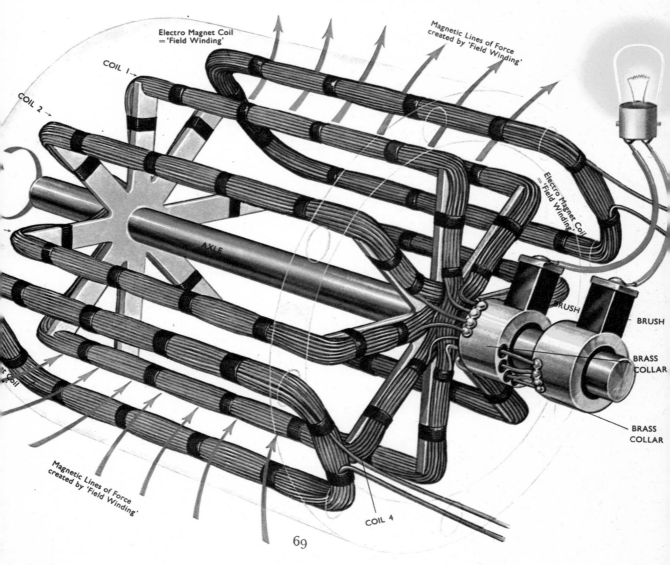

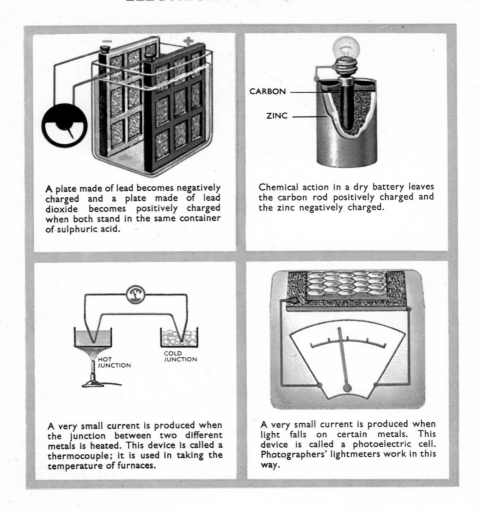

A plate made of lead becomes negatively charged and a plate made of lead dioxide becomes positively charged when both stand in the same container of sulphuric acid.

Chemical action in a dry battery leaves the carbon rod positively charged and the zinc negatively charged.

A very small current is produced when the junction between two different metals is heated. This device is called a thermocouple; it is used in taking the temperature of furnaces.

A very small current is produced when light falls on certain metals. This device is called a photoelectric cell. Photographers' lightmeters work in this way.

electromagnets. An electromagnet consists of a coil known as the field winding (i.e. winding to make a magnetic field) wound onto an iron core. Such a coil has a magnetic field through its centre when a current passes round the wire, and the field is usually much stronger than that of an ordinary magnet.

How do the electromagnets get *their* supply of current? In a generating station it is usual to have a small extra generator on the same driving axle, and this has *permanent* magnets to give it its field.

How is the outside circuit (e.g. the lamp in the picture) connected to the moving coils? At first sight this seems a difficult problem. It is solved by connecting the ends of each coil to a pair of brass collars mounted on the axle that turns the coils. The outside circuit is connected to 'brushes' (either soft blocks of carbon or metal springs) which rub against the rotating brass collars.

70

CHAPTER TWENTY

The Principle of D.C. Electric Motors

DIRECT-CURRENT motors, like direct-current generators are made from magnets and coils of wire. In the generator, a coil moves between the poles of a magnet and causes an electric current to flow in the coil. The motor is the exact reverse. A *current flowing in a coil*

produces movement. The current in the coil makes it behave as though it were a magnet, with its own north and south poles. These poles attract or repel the poles of fixed ordinary magnets, and the combination of attractive and repulsive forces rotates the coil.

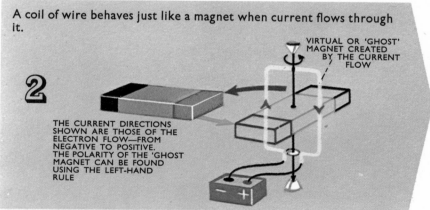

Like poles repel, unlike poles attract, and the movable magnet starts to rotate.

ATTRACTION

REPULSION

IN ALL THE DIAGRAMS BLUE ARROWS INDICATE THE REPULSIVE FORCE BETWEEN LIKE POLES AND PURPLE ARROWS THE ATTRACTIVE FORCE BETWEEN UNLIKE POLES

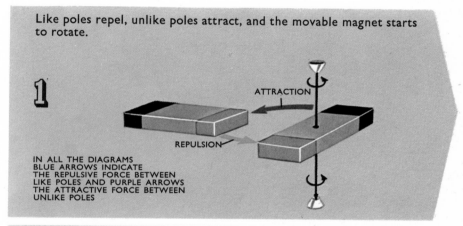

A coil of wire behaves just like a magnet when current flows through it.

VIRTUAL OR 'GHOST' MAGNET CREATED BY THE CURRENT FLOW

THE CURRENT DIRECTIONS SHOWN ARE THOSE OF THE ELECTRON FLOW—FROM NEGATIVE TO POSITIVE. THE POLARITY OF THE 'GHOST' MAGNET CAN BE FOUND USING THE LEFT-HAND RULE

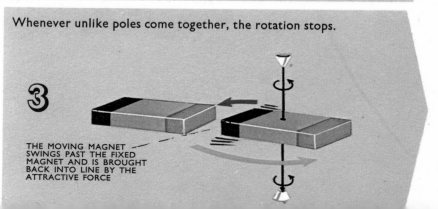

Whenever unlike poles come together, the rotation stops.

THE MOVING MAGNET SWINGS PAST THE FIXED MAGNET AND IS BROUGHT BACK INTO LINE BY THE ATTRACTIVE FORCE

The coil's rotation stops when unlike poles come together.

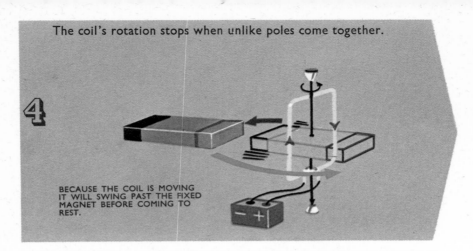

4

BECAUSE THE COIL IS MOVING
IT WILL SWING PAST THE FIXED
MAGNET BEFORE COMING TO
REST.

The magnet now rotates between two opposite poles. A doubled force acts on it.

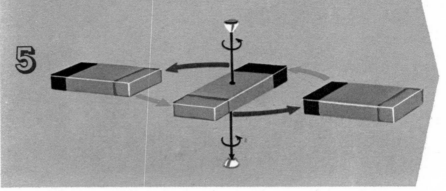

5

Similarly, a doubled force acts on the coil of wire.

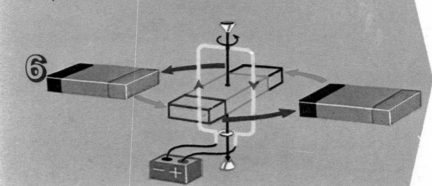

6

Unlike poles come together, and the magnet swings past the fixed pole before finally coming back to rest in line with the fixed magnet.

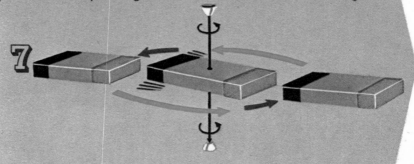

7

The coil will also swing past. If nothing else happens, the coil will come back to rest in line. But . . .

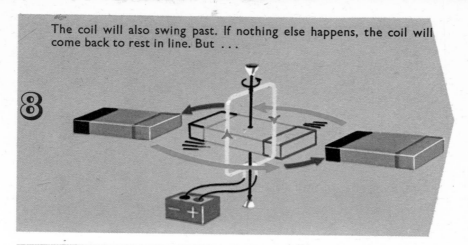

. . . at this instant the battery terminals are changed. The polarity of the 'ghost' magnet changes. Each end is now repelled (like poles repel) and the coil continues to rotate.

THIS IS THE SAME END OF THE MAGNET OPPOSITE THE NORTH POLE AS IN 8—ONLY THE POLARITY HAS CHANGED

THE BATTERY TERMINALS HAVE BEEN CHANGED AND CURRENT NOW FLOWS IN THE OPPO- SITE DIRECTION

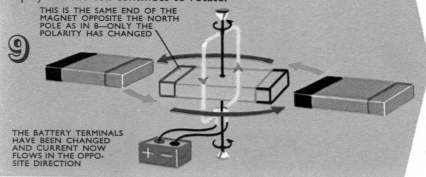

The coil has now rotated through half a complete revolution. It continues until unlike poles come together again . . .

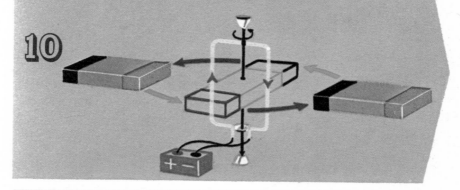

. . . when the battery terminals are again switched and the polarity is reversed. Now like poles (which repel) are together and the rotation continues.

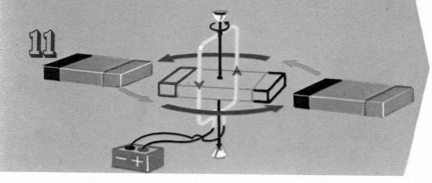

The magnets come into line again, and the direction of current flow is changed a third time.

12

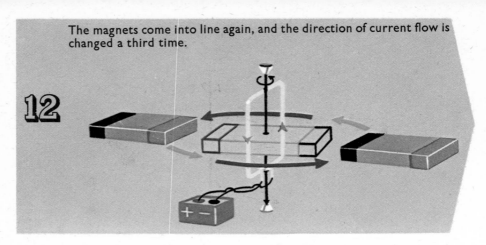

After the fourth change. The battery terminals must be changed twice every complete rotation.

13

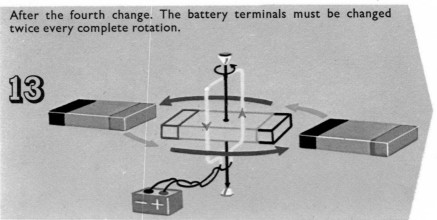

The coil will go on rotating provided the direction of current flow is changed whenever unlike poles come together.

14

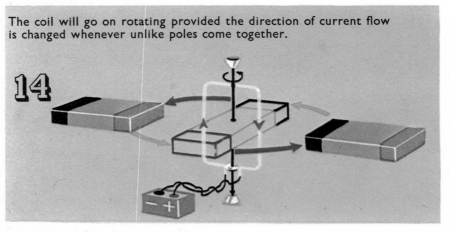

We can tell which pole is which by holding the coil in the *left* hand, so that the fingers wrap round it, pointing in the same direction as the electron flow (from negative to positive). The thumb will then point to the north pole.

The Left Hand Rule

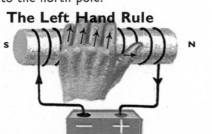

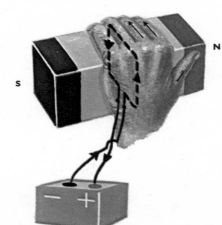

74

The rotation of a coil carrying a D.C. current in a magnetic field could continue indefinitely provided the *direction* of the current was changed twice every rotation – in fact whenever the *plane* of the coil was at right angles to the magnetic field.

The device which automatically changes the direction of current flow, and hence the polarity of the 'ghost' magnet is called a *commutator*. In the simple, one-coil electric motor the commutator consists of two semi-circular pieces of metal, separated by an air gap, which rotate between two fixed electrical contacts. Twice every rotation the contacts cross the gap in the commutator and so switch the direction of the flow of current round the coil.

A one-coil motor will not run very smoothly, since the magnetic forces which rotate it vary with the relative position of coil and magnets. Twice every rotation it will jerk when the commutator switches the current. For increased power as well as smoothness of operation, the rotating part of D.C. motors is made from many coils of wire, insulated from each other. (The coils of wire are of course wound from one continuous length of insulated wire). The framework on which the coils are wound is called an *armature*, and is usually made of soft iron, which has the effect of concentrating the electromagnetic field between the two pole pieces, and which loses its magnetism very quickly (this is necessary as the magnetisation is to be altered twice every complete rotation). The coils

The commutator in a many-coiled motor is arranged so that whenever a coil's plane is at right angles to a line joining the magnets, the direction of current flowing in that particular coil is reversed.

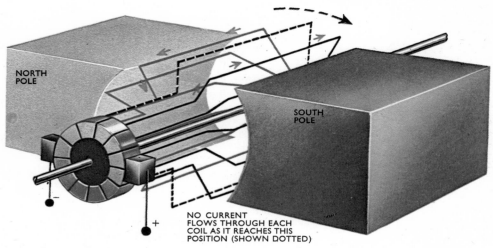

NORTH POLE

SOUTH POLE

NO CURRENT FLOWS THROUGH EACH COIL AS IT REACHES THIS POSITION (SHOWN DOTTED)

are wound in a complicated way so that all the wires near the same magnetic pole carry currents in the same direction, and the armature winding acts like a single coil with a single 'ghost' magnet nearly in line with the two fixed magnets. For this purpose, the commutator is divided into many copper strips, separated by mica, an insulating material. The two contacts are made from carbon.

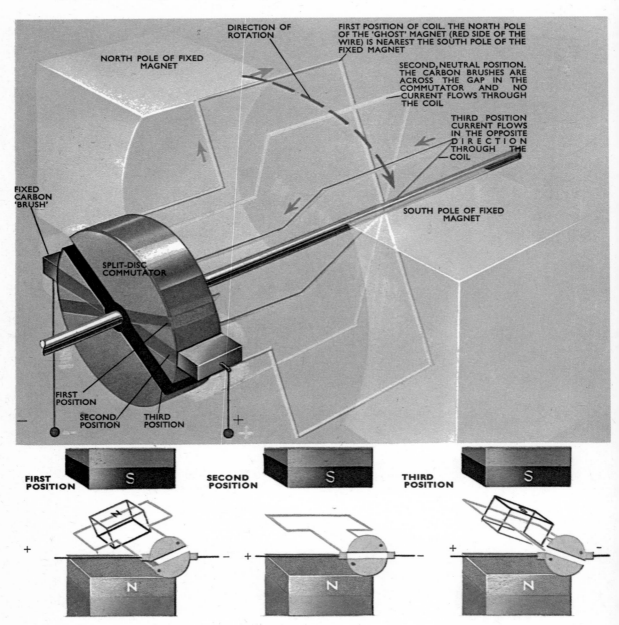

DIRECTION OF ROTATION

NORTH POLE OF FIXED MAGNET

FIRST POSITION OF COIL. THE NORTH POLE OF THE 'GHOST' MAGNET (RED SIDE OF THE WIRE) IS NEAREST THE SOUTH POLE OF THE FIXED MAGNET

SECOND, NEUTRAL POSITION. THE CARBON BRUSHES ARE ACROSS THE GAP IN THE COMMUTATOR AND NO CURRENT FLOWS THROUGH THE COIL

THIRD POSITION CURRENT FLOWS IN THE OPPOSITE DIRECTION THROUGH THE COIL

FIXED CARBON 'BRUSH'

SPLIT-DISC COMMUTATOR

SOUTH POLE OF FIXED MAGNET

FIRST POSITION

SECOND POSITION

THIRD POSITION

FIRST POSITION

SECOND POSITION

THIRD POSITION

A commutator for a single-coil motor. The direction of the current flowing in the coil is reversed when the gap in the commutator passes between the carbon brushes.

IN electromagnetism there are two basic principles which mean ultimately exactly the same thing. One is the motor principle—*a current flowing in a wire through a magnetic field produces movement*. The other is the generator or dynamo principle—*when a wire moves through a magnetic field a current is produced in the wire*. In other words:

Motor principle:
    current + field ⟶ movement
Generator principle:
    movement + field ⟶ current

It was shown how the motor principle works – how a coil of wire would start to rotate in a magnetic field if a current of electricity were passed round it.

Once the motor coil is moving, however, it has the two things—movement and field – needed to bring the generator principle into operation, and the result of movement and field is a current flowing in the motor coil. This is an extra current, distinct from the steady direct current driving the coil.

In which direction does this extra current flow? The direction can be deduced from the principle that something cannot be produced from nothing. In order to move the motor coil, it is given electrical energy from a direct current source.

Now there are only two directions in which the current produced by the generating action could possibly flow —either in the same direction as the direct current, or in the opposite direction. If it flows with the direct current, it increases the effective current driving the motor, which increases the speed of rotation, which

increases the generated current, and so on, so that the coil will move faster and faster without limit. It will then have an infinite amount of kinetic (moving) energy, no matter how much (or how little) energy is supplied by the driving current. This contravenes the something-for-nothing principle. So the generated current must flow in the opposite direction. It must always *oppose* the driving current.

The motor *commutator* changes the direction of the direct current twice every rotation, so the direction of the opposing generated current is also changed twice every rotation.

Thus once the coil is moving it will act as though it contained a separate source of electric current. Sources of electric current are differences in electrical potential or voltage. An alternative name for the difference in electric potential is *electromotive force* (e.m.f.)—literally the force which moves the electrons constituting the electric current. Because the e.m.f. resulting from the generating action opposes the e.m.f., or difference in electric potential supplying the direct (driving) current, it is called the BACK E.M.F.

The back e.m.f. limits the speed of the motor, since it puts an effective brake on the amount of current the motor can receive. The opposing e.m.f. will, in fact, be nearly as big as the driving e.m.f. If a 240-volt D.C. supply drives the motor, then, when the motor is running, the back e.m.f. will be about 230 volts. So the *effective* e.m.f. is only 10 volts.

However, the current often *needs* to be limited. The coils of wire have a

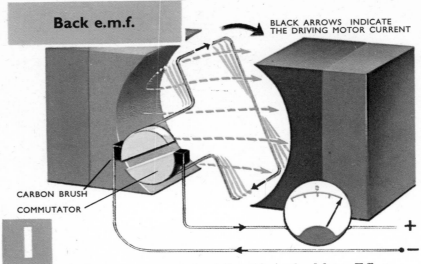

BLACK ARROWS INDICATE
THE DRIVING MOTOR CURRENT

CARBON BRUSH

COMMUTATOR

1 *A direct current moves a coil—this is the Motor Effect.*

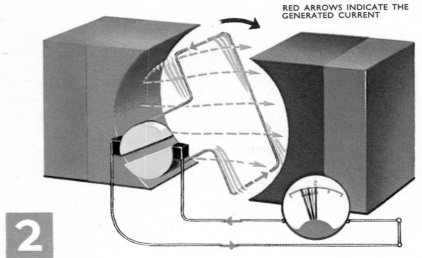

RED ARROWS INDICATE THE
GENERATED CURRENT

2 *The moving coil generates a current in the opposite direction.*

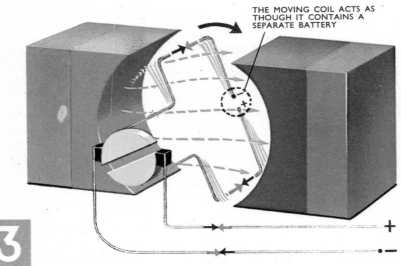

THE MOVING COIL ACTS AS
THOUGH IT CONTAINS A
SEPARATE BATTERY

3 *The generated current opposes the driving (motor) current.*

very low resistance (about 1 ohm). Say the driving voltage is 240 volts, and there is no back e.m.f. Then applying Ohm's law to the coil:

$$\text{voltage} = \text{current} \times \text{resistance}$$
$$240 \text{ volts} = \text{current (amps)} \times 1 \text{ ohm}$$
$$\text{current} = 240 \text{ amps}$$

This is a very large current, and one which would very rapidly burn out the coil.

Applying Ohm's law to the coil with the back e.m.f. in operation:

$$\text{voltage} = \text{current} \times \text{resistance}$$
$$(240 - 230) \text{ volts} = \text{current (amps)} \times 1 \text{ ohm}$$
$$\text{current} = 10 \text{ amps}$$

which the coil will be able to stand.

The current through the coil will be about 10 amps when the coil is moving at full speed. But when the motor is just starting, its speed, and hence its back e.m.f., will be very low.

Starting Resistance

When the D.C. motor is running it generates a back e.m.f. which limits the amount of current flowing through the coil. However, when the motor is just starting, it will take time to build up its speed, and its back e.m.f. During this time the current through the coil would be very high indeed, were it not for the starting resistance. This controls the current flowing through the coil. In the first diagram the motor is almost stationary, and the current is limited by passing it through the whole of the starting resistance. As the motor picks up speed and the back e.m.f. increases, the resistance can be gradually decreased until, as in the final diagram, the motor is running at full speed and the resistance is completely shorted out of the circuit. Since the current flowing through the coil determines its speed of rotation, the starting resistance can be used to vary the speed of the motor.

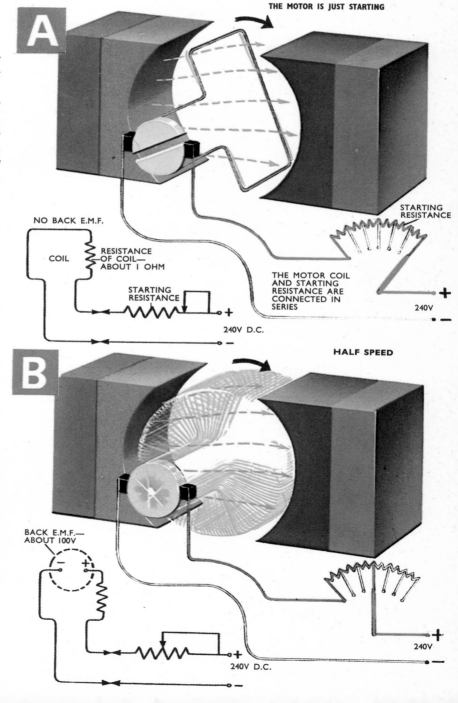

A

THE MOTOR IS JUST STARTING

NO BACK E.M.F.

COIL

RESISTANCE OF COIL— ABOUT 1 OHM

STARTING RESISTANCE

240V D.C.

STARTING RESISTANCE

THE MOTOR COIL AND STARTING RESISTANCE ARE CONNECTED IN SERIES

240V

B

HALF SPEED

BACK E.M.F.— ABOUT 100V

240V D.C.

240V

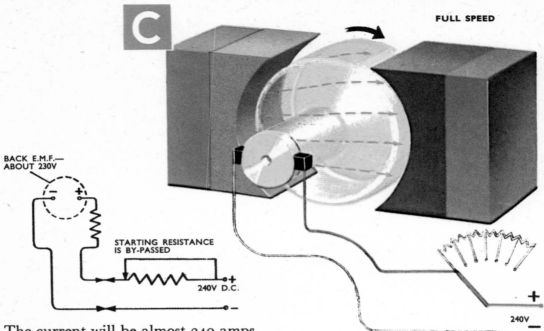

BACK E.M.F.—
ABOUT 230V

STARTING RESISTANCE
IS BY-PASSED

240V D.C.

+

240V

The current will be almost 240 amps, which, as has been mentioned, is far too large for the coil to withstand. While the motor is building up its speed (and its back e.m.f.), therefore, some means must be found of lowering the current. This is done in practice by adding some extra electrical resistance to the coil—reducing the current by increasing the opposition to its flow. The extra resistance is called a *starting resistance*. It is a separate resistance, included in *series* with the motor coil. As the motor speeds up, the back e.m.f. increases, and the starting resistance can be gradually reduced until the motor is operating under full power and at full speed.

D.C. Motors – Series and Shunt

A coil of wire with a current flowing round it acts like a magnet. In the D.C. motor there were three magnets – two fixed permanent magnets and the 'ghost' electro-magnet which was illustrated as a 'ghost' to indicate the magnetic field, the result of the direct current's flowing round the rotating coil. The force which turned the coil came from the interaction of two magnetic fields – the stationary field of the permanent magnets and the rotating field of the single coil. When a commutator was added to the motor and the number of coils on the rotating part (called the *armature*) was increased the rotating field could be made to stay still while the armature moved. A steady, constant force then acted on the armature, which steadily rotated at a speed determined by the amount of current flowing in its coils. Reversing the direction of the current reversed the motor.

In most practicable D.C. electric motors the two permanent magnets are replaced by electro-magnets. The shaped soft-iron pole-pieces become magnetized when a current is passed through the coils of wire wound round them. To create a steady field like the magnets they replace, the electro-magnets must be magnetized with *direct current*. Thus all the parts of the motor operate on direct current, and obviously they will all be connected to the same D.C. supply. The coils wound around the electro-magnets (the *field windings*) and the coils wound around the armature (called the *armature windings*) are in fact connected to one another. Only the *armature* current must pass through the commutator to reverse its direction twice per rotation: the current through the field windings is not reversed. There are three basic ways in which armature and field windings can be connected, and which distinguish the three common types of direct-current motors – *series-wound*, *shunt-wound* and *compound-wound*.

In the series-wound motor the windings are connected in series – they form one continuous circuit and the same current flows through all of them. And since the field windings carry the same heavy current driving the motor, the field windings are made from a few turns of very thick wire.

In the shunt motor field windings and armature windings are connected in *parallel* across the power supply. The field windings are said to be *shunted* across the armature windings, and the currents flowing in them are different. The field current (in the electro-magnets) is in practice much less than the current in the armature and is independent of it. In this way the shunt-wound motor behaves very much like a D.C. motor with permanent magnets as pole pieces. The field windings are made from a great many turns of fine wire as they do not have to stand up to a very heavy current.

The compound-wound motor, as its name suggests, has its field wind-ings and armature windings connected in series and in parallel at the same time.

One of the many advantages of using electro-magnets in place of permanent magnets is that a north-pole piece can be changed to a south-pole piece and *vice-versa* by reversing the direction in which current flows round it. It gives an alternative method of reversing the motor (it can also be reversed by changing the direction of current through the armature windings). This, of course, applies only to shunt- and compound-wound motors. Reversing the current through a series motor reverses the current through all of the windings and the net result is that the motor continues to rotate as before.

The speed of the motor depends on the current supplied to *all* the windings, because the magnetic field in each increases with the current. So in shunt and compound motors the speed can be varied by a rheostat, or variable resistance in the field circuit. This is generally preferable to changing the armature current with the starting resistance.

What useful purpose do these different windings serve? It must be remembered that the function of any motor is to do work, and the different methods of connection fit the motor for particular kinds of work. The two important factors in the performance of the motor are its *speed* and *torque* (turning force) which it transfers along its shaft to move a machine, called the *load*. The way in which current flows around the motor coils alters the way the speed and the torque vary.

The speed of the motor depends on the currents flowing through all the

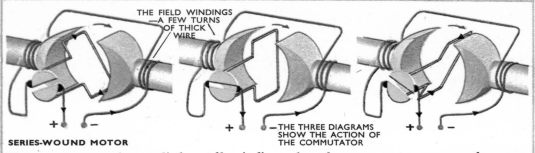

THE FIELD WINDINGS
—A FEW TURNS
OF THICK
WIRE

—THE THREE DIAGRAMS
SHOW THE ACTION OF
THE COMMUTATOR

SERIES-WOUND MOTOR

The same current is supplied to all windings, but the commutator reverses the current through the rotating armature.

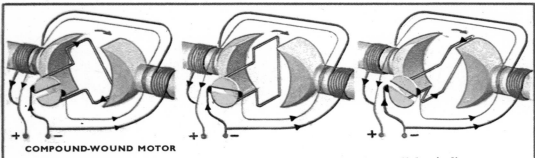

COMPOUND-WOUND MOTOR

The field electro-magnets are magnetised by both series and parallel windings.

windings. In the series-wound motor the same current flows through the field windings and via the commutator, through the armature windings. The device which alters the current supply – it may be simply an extra, variable resistance, or rheostat – automatically alters the magnetic fields produced by both the windings. Because both fields are increasing and decreasing *at the same time* the turning force, or *torque* will alter considerably, and by increasing the current by even a small amount, the motor will rapidly accelerate. It would start to rotate dangerously fast if the torque

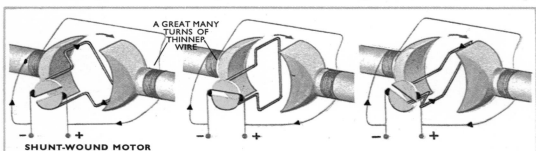

A GREAT MANY
TURNS OF
THINNER
WIRE

SHUNT-WOUND MOTOR

The field windings are shunted across the armature windings. A different current flows in each.

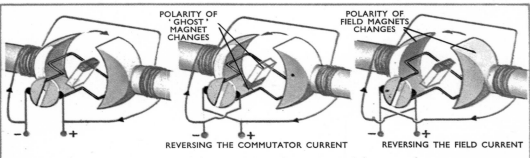

POLARITY OF
'GHOST'
MAGNET
CHANGES

POLARITY OF
FIELD MAGNETS
CHANGES

REVERSING THE COMMUTATOR CURRENT

REVERSING THE FIELD CURRENT

A shunt motor can be reversed by reversing the current either *to the commutator, or to the field magnets.*

had to rotate only the relatively light armature. So the large starting torque is controlled by initially connecting the motor to a machine driving a heavy load. The speed of a series-connected D.C. motor is very sensitive not only to changes in the current, but also to changes in its load. It runs slowly with a heavy load and quickly with a light load. Series-wound motors are used, therefore, when a load has to be *accelerated* quickly rather than *moved* quickly. A good example of this is the crane or excavator where the heavy load is lifted from rest. They are also used in electric trains, because of the very rapid acceleration this type of motor can give.

In the shunt-wound motor, on the other hand, the driving current in the armature is independent of the field current. Initially the armature current is limited by the starting resistance, and as the current in both windings is small the starting force developed by the motor is small. It cannot be used to move a heavy load from rest, as the series motor did.

The shunt motor is used where it is possible for it to be started and operating at full speed before it is connected to the machine it has to operate. Because the current in the field windings is constant and the current through the armature windings is initially limited by the starting resistance, the motor will rotate at a practically constant speed, no matter what load it is driving. These characteristics are also found in motors using *alternating* current (A.C.) rather than direct current. Since alternating current has practically replaced direct current in the electricity supply, D.C. shunt-wound motors are very seldom used for large installations. One application is the iron lung where the motor must rotate at constant speed to breathe steadily for the paralysed patient.

The compound motor is used when the better characteristics of both series and shunt are to be exploited. They combine the high initial torque of the series motor with the steady final speed of the shunt motor.

In the series-wound motor, the field windings are connected in series with the armature (via the commutator), and the currents in both windings are the same. When a small current flows in the armature, a small current flows in the field windings so the field in which the armature rotates will be small. Now the back e.m.f. which limits the amount of current, and which is generated by the moving coil, depends on the *field* and on the *speed of rotation*. A very small current is required to rotate the light armature. If there is no load connected to the shaft of the motor, the motor will speed dangerously fast, but not fast enough, because of the weak field, to generate enough back e.m.f. to limit the current and stabilise the speed of the motor. So series connected motors must always be started with the load connected and the load must never be put on or taken off while the motor is running.

In the shunt-wound motor the field windings are shunted across the armature, and the currents flowing in them will be different and almost completely independent of each other. Altering the current flowing to the commutator and armature by altering the starting resistance will not affect the current through the field windings. When the power supply is first switched on, the current through the field windings will almost immediately assume its full working value. It creates a larger initial field than in the series-wound motor, so the back e.m.f. generated by the moving armature will be greater. This will tend to control the speed of the motor, and, no matter what load is connected to the shaft of the motor, the motor's speed will be virtually dictated by the operating current. In fact the speed under normal or 'full' load is only about 10% smaller than the speed with no load at all. Because of this the shunt-wound motor is called a *constant speed* motor.

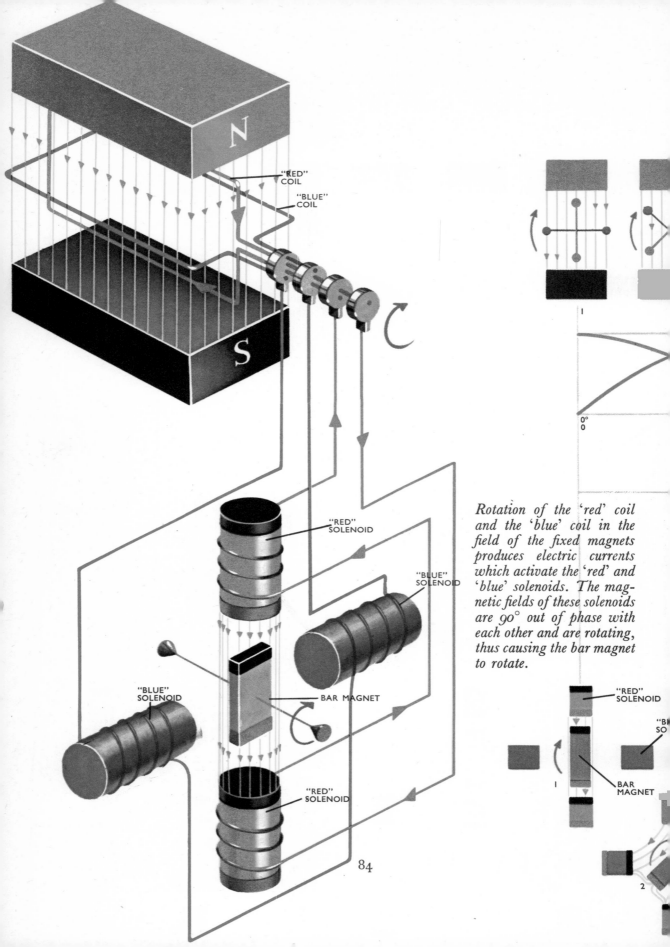

N

"RED"
COIL

"BLUE"
COIL

S

"RED"
SOLENOID

"BLUE"
SOLENOID

"BLUE"
SOLENOID

BAR MAGNET

"RED"
SOLENOID

Rotation of the 'red' coil
and the 'blue' coil in the
field of the fixed magnets
produces electric currents
which activate the 'red' and
'blue' solenoids. The magnetic fields of these solenoids
are 90° out of phase with
each other and are rotating,
thus causing the bar magnet
to rotate.

"RED"
SOLENOID

"B"
SO

BAR
MAGNET

I

2

84

CHAPTER TWENTY-ONE

The Motor which Synchronises
with the Mains

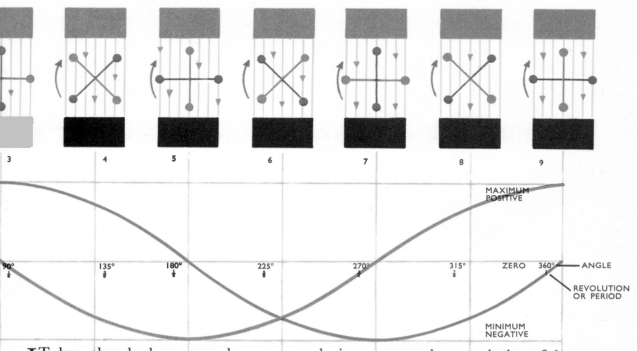

IT has already been seen how an alternating voltage is generated in a coil which rotates in a magnetic field. If two similar coils are mounted on the same axis but at right angles to each other, as shown at the top left of the diagram, and the two coils are rotated together in the magnetic field, separate alternating voltages will be generated or *induced* in the two coils. In the diagram are shown nine stages during one complete revolution of the generator coils and immediately below this can be seen how the size of the induced voltage varies for each of the coils. For example, when the voltage induced in the blue coil is zero, the voltage induced in the red coil will be maximum. This is because the sides of the blue coil are moving parallel to and are therefore not cutting the lines of magnetic force or flux,

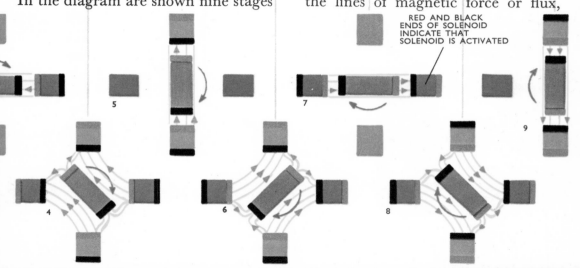

RED AND BLACK
ENDS OF SOLENOID
INDICATE THAT
SOLENOID IS ACTIVATED

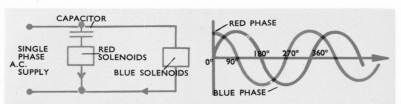

When an alternating voltage is applied to a capacitor, the current is 90° out of phase with the voltage. This fact is used to produce the two out-of-phase currents necessary to drive a motor. The blue solenoids would, for example, be connected directly across a single-phase a.c. supply and the red solenoids in series with a capacitor across the same supply. Blue circuit current would then have been out of phase with red circuit current and a rotating magnetic field would have been obtained as before.

This method of producing, in effect, two phases from a single phase supply is in common use.

whilst the lines of flux are being cut at the maximum rate by the sides of the red coil. The voltages induced in the two coils are then said to have a *phase difference* of 90°. In other words, the voltage in the red coil reaches a particular value – say maximum positive – $\frac{1}{4}$ of a revolution or *period* before the blue coil attains the same size. The arrangement is known as a *two-phase generator* or *two-phase alternator*, with each coil generating a voltage *out of phase* by 90°, with the other.

Earlier it was seen that a coil carrying an electric current behaves as if it were a bar magnet. The strength of the electromagnet is determined by the number of turns of wire in the coil and the size of the electric current which flows. The magnetic polarity is fixed by the direction of the current flow, with the North Pole always at the same end of the coil for the same direction of flow of current. If, however, an alternating current is made to flow in the coil, the strength and polarity of the magnetic field which will be produced will change in sympathy with the changing current. In other words, when the current flows in one direction, one end of the

coil will act as a North Pole, and when it flows the other way, the same end will act as a South Pole.

What happens when a two-phase alternator is connected to four similar solenoids arranged as is shown in the lower left of the diagram? Here, the red solenoids are connected in series with the red coil, and the blue solenoids are connected in series with the blue coil of the alternator. The bar magnet is placed so that it is in the magnetic fields produced by the coils, and is suspended so that it can turn freely in the plane of the coils. As the alternator rotates, magnetic fields will be set up by the solenoid coils, and the size of the field in each coil will depend on the current induced in them by the alternator. There will be nine separate stages, and each is shown in the diagram. At stage 1, red circuit current will be a maximum because the red alternator coil is at right angles to the field of the alternator magnet. The red solenoid field will therefore be a maximum and the polarity will be as indicated. Since blue coil voltage is zero at this instant, blue circuit current and hence blue solenoid field will be zero. The bar magnet will therefore take up the position shown, with unlike poles attracting. At stage 2, red and blue solenoid fields will be equal and so the bar magnet will have moved to the mid position shown. At stage 3, red solenoid field will have fallen to zero but blue solenoid field will have increased to maximum. The bar magnet will therefore now lie along the blue solenoid axis. And so on through the nine stages. The bar magnet has faithfully followed the rotation of the alternator coils through all the stages. This means that the magnetic field which has been turning the bar magnet has faithfully followed the rotation of the alternator coils, so a *rotating* magnetic field has been produced by the four *stationary* solenoids.

Since the *rotor*, i.e. the bar magnet, of a simple A.C. Motor rotates in exact sympathy or in *synchronism* with the A.C. supply, this type of machine is called a *synchronous* motor. In practice it is usual to use an electro-magnetic rather than a permanent magnet rotor. Then, the direct current for the rotor coils is supplied via brushes and *slip rings* similar to those used for the alternator above.

The Induction Motor

Something like 90% of all the electric motors that are made each year are what are called *induction motors*, and it would be interesting to see what special features this type of motor has which make it so much more popular than all other types of electric motor, A.C. and D.C., put together.

The principle of *electromagnetic induction* has already been explained.

If a closed loop of wire is rotated in a fixed magnetic field, an electric current will be *induced* which will flow round the coil. Whenever an electric current flows in a conductor it sets up a magnetic field, so that in addition to the fixed magnetic field already present there will be another one due to this induced current. The two fields cannot exist separately side by side, but combine to form a *resultant* field.

This resultant field is distorted as shown in the diagram. The shapes of the lines of force which result may be explained by the fact that opposing lines of force tend to neutralise each other, whereas the lines of force running in the same direction augment each other.

In a region of strong magnetic field, the lines of force are close together; in the region of a weak field, they are more widely separated.

In general, there is a tendency for a magnetic field to try to remove these distortions (just as air rushes in to occupy a vacuum), and this leads to distorted lines trying to straighten themselves out, and lines which are close together try to repel each other, so that the lines of force all become equally spaced. In other words, the tendency is to try to create a *uniform magnetic field*.

In the resultant field produced by the coil and the magnet, the two fields act to produce a region of zero magnetic field strength behind the moving coil and an intensified region in front of the conductor.

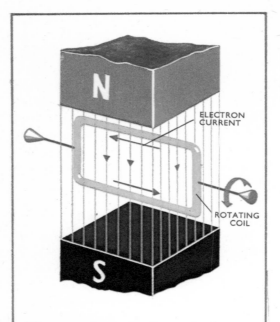

When a coil is rotated in a fixed magnetic field a current is induced in the coil because the moving conductor is cutting lines of magnetic force or flux.

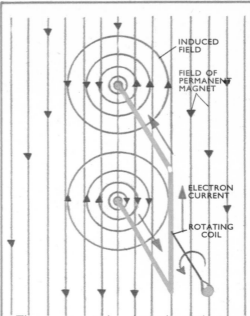

The current induced in the coil gives rise to an additional set of lines of magnetic force.

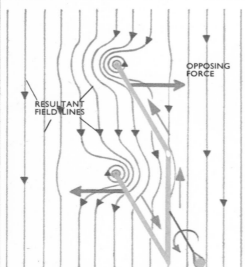

The additional set of lines of magnetic force combines with the set from the fixed magnetic field to produce a *resultant* field. The distortions in this produce a force on the moving conductor which opposes its motion.

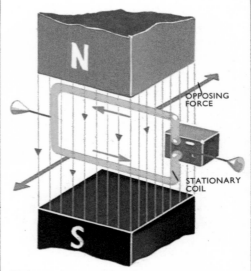

If the coil were stationary and it carried a current equal in magnitude and direction to the induced current, a force equal to the opposing force (above) would result which would make the coil rotate in the field.

In the process of trying to produce a uniform magnetic field, a force is produced on the conductor which opposes its motion (for it is the motion of the coil which produces the distorted field). It must be emphasized that this force only acts against the motion, it is not sufficient to stop it; after all, the force only exists in the first place because of the motion.

If the loop of wire had been stationary in the magnetic field and the same size of current was made to flow by inserting a battery in the loop, the same resultant magnetic field would have been obtained. This being so, the same force would have acted on each side of the loop and so the initially stationary loop would have been made to move in the direction of this force. In short, a motor effect would have been created.

Take the argument a little further now. It was supposed in the first place that the magnetic field due to the bar magnets was stationary and that the loop of wire was rotating. Suppose now that the *wire* is initially stationary and that the *magnetic field* is rotating at the same speed but in the opposite direction to that of the loop first described, as in a synchronous motor. Because the *relative* motion of the loop and the lines of force is the same as before, the *moving lines of force* are now being cut by the stationary sides of the loop at exactly the same rate and in the same direction. The induced current in the coil will in consequence be of exactly the same size and direction as before. This means, of course, that the forces on the coil will be the

If the coil is stationary, and the magnetic field *is made to rotate, a current is induced in the coil, and the coil will rotate.*

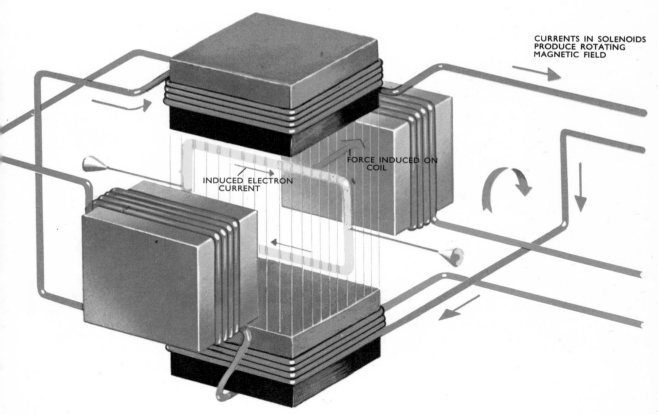

CURRENTS IN SOLENOIDS
PRODUCE ROTATING
MAGNETIC FIELD

FORCE INDUCED ON COIL

INDUCED ELECTRON CURRENT

The Squirrel-Cage Motor

In practical machines a single loop of wire would not make for very great efficiency, so the squirrel-cage construction is used. This consists of a large number of copper (or aluminium) rods whose ends are fixed to two copper or aluminium rings.

An iron core is used to strengthen the magnetic field.

same, in size and direction, as before, and so the freely pivoted wire will start to turn in the same direction as that of the rotating magnetic field. As the loop turns faster and faster, it will try to 'catch up' with the rotating field, and the *difference* between its speed and that of the

rotating field will get smaller and smaller. The size of the induced current and hence also the force will thus fall. The loop of wire will settle down to a steady but lower speed than that of the rotating field. This steady speed will not be as great as that of the rotating field because the driving force due to the induced current not only drives the loop in rotation, but has to overcome frictional rotation in the bearings of the motor and air resistance as well as to drive any load attached to the motor.

The induction motor is so called because the driving force is due to a current *induced* in the rotor by its interaction with the magnetic field. In other types of electric motor the driving force is due to current supplied to the rotor directly from the mains by means of brushes and *slip rings* or commutators. It is this absence of brushes, etc., in the induction motor that enables a simple robust machine to be constructed for low cost and virtually no maintenance.

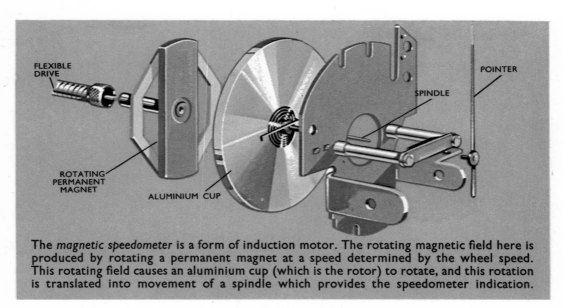

The *magnetic speedometer* is a form of induction motor. The rotating magnetic field here is produced by rotating a permanent magnet at a speed determined by the wheel speed. This rotating field causes an aluminium cup (which is the rotor) to rotate, and this rotation is translated into movement of a spindle which provides the speedometer indication.

Static Electricity

CHAPTER TWENTY-TWO

Friction can make an Electric Charge

FRICTION between two objects sometimes leads to the transfer of electrons from one to the other. Electrons are units of negative electric charge, and the object which gains them gains a negative charge, while the other becomes positively charged. No charge has been added to or taken away from the system. The amount of positive charge on one object is equal to the amount of negative charge transferred to the other. If the object is made from material (e.g. copper) which conducts electricity, electrons immediately leak away through it and the charge on its surface is destroyed. A rubbed metal rod, for instance, will not attract small pieces of paper – it cannot keep its charges. But if the object is made from some kind of insulating material (e.g. plastic), electrons cannot leak away through it. Any charges put on its surface have to stay there. A plastic pen that has

Charge rubbed from a rotating ball is conducted along a metal pipe and the man at the other end gets an electric shock. The jar of water which the man is holding is an attempt to store charge. From it developed the Leyden jar and the modern capacitor.

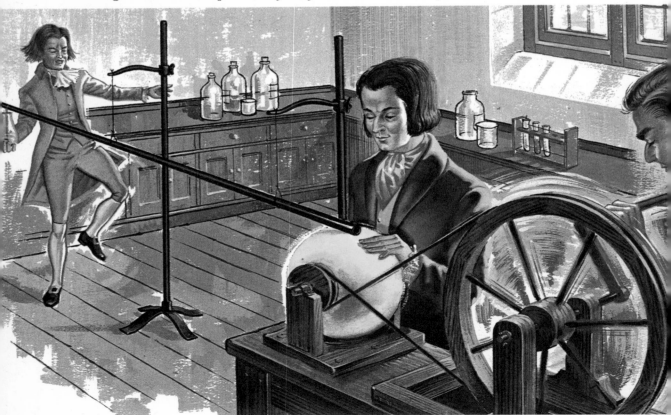

been rubbed will attract small pieces of paper simply because it has been charged and has kept its charges. Objects similarly charged (i.e. negative and negative) repel one another, while those with charges of opposite sign attract one another. This is called *static* electricity because the charges do not flow, as in current electricity, but, if they do move at all, move only a very small distance.

Electrons object to being herded together. They are all negatively charged and repel each other. If there is a possible escape route by which electrons can move away from one another, they will take it. When a negatively charged insulator is touched, the transferred, or excess, electrons will flow through the finger, through the body, to earth, and the insulator loses its charge. The flow of electrons is an electric current, far smaller than the electric currents produced by dynamos or batteries. Until the end of the eighteenth century it was, however, the only kind of electricity known. It could be produced by rubbing a glass rod with silk, or an amber rod with fur. This is the first and simplest form of friction machine. Whether the rods become positively or negatively charged depends on what they are rubbed with, and which of the two substances loses electrons more easily.

The more a rod is rubbed, the more charge it accumulates. The amount of charge the rod will hold is limited by the insulation between the rod and the hand holding it, and the rod and the air. The charge tends to leak away because the insulation is not perfect. In the eighteenth century more efficient methods of producing friction, or static, electricity were devised. Guericke made a large ball

Guericke's sulphur ball becomes charged by rubbing. When it discharges it sparks and crackles.

of sulphur (an insulator), rotated it with one hand and rubbed it with the other. The large ball could hold a large amount of charge, and it could

In the simplest form of friction machine a glass rod is rubbed with silk. The friction between the rod and the silk causes the transfer of electrons from the rod to the silk. The rod has a positive electric charge, while the silk has an equal negative charge. Rod and silk will attract one another, since they carry charges of opposite sign. (Charges of the *same* sign *repel*.)

The charged rod will attract light objects, such as pieces of paper. Like all matter, the paper consists of atoms with heavy, positively charged nuclei and light, negatively charged electrons around them. The paper is neutral—it carries no net positive or negative charge. Suppose the rod is positively charged. It will repel the nuclei and attract the electrons. The electrons move towards the rod, while the heavier nuclei are slightly displaced away from it. The charges are induced to move, and the rod need not *touch* the paper to move them. Unlike charges are now closest to one another, and the paper will be attracted and move towards the rod. If the rod were negatively charged, the parts of the paper nearest to it would gain an induced positive charge, and paper and rod would still attract one another.

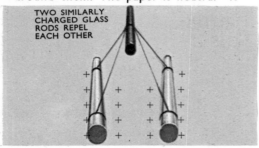

TWO SIMILARLY CHARGED GLASS RODS REPEL EACH OTHER

A CHARGED ROD ATTRACTS PIECES OF PAPER

be discharged by holding a conductor leading to earth near to it. The repulsive force between electrons becomes so great that they are able to jump across the air gap, and appear as a spark. Clouds charged with static electricity also lose their charge by means of an electric spark which we call lightning.

Larger machines were made and larger amounts of electricity were produced. Now a means of storing charge so that it could be used when required was needed. The first device made was the Leyden jar. This was a glass jar coated inside and out with metal foil. The inner coating was connected to the friction machine and electrons transferred by friction flowed to the inner coating and remained there. When the jar could hold no more charge, the lead to the machine was cut off, the jar was insulated and the charges in it stored for future use. The modern capacitor or condenser is the same in principle as the Leyden jar – it has two conducting layers separated by an insulator.

CHAPTER TWENTY-THREE

The Gold Leaf Electroscope

WHEN an ebonite or glass rod is rubbed with a piece of fur, some of the loosely bound electrons that are attached to the fur become dislodged and attach themselves to the surface of the glass. The glass, with its extra electrons, is negatively charged. The fur, with its deficiency of negatively charged electrons, has an overall positive charge. After rubbing, both fur and glass carry *electrostatic charges*.

The gold leaf electroscope was invented in 1787 to detect the presence of such electrostatic charges. It can be used to find out whether a charge is positive or negative and to compare the sizes of different charges. It does not measure their actual values. This is done by an instrument called an electrometer.

The gold leaf electroscope works on the principle that positive charges repel each other; so do negative charges. (It is only unlike charges that attract.) If a positive charge is put on to two flimsy pieces of gold leaf they repel each other. The greater the charge, the more they separate. Exactly the same happens if the leaves are negatively charged.

The apparatus. Because they are so flimsy and will be blown about and ripped by draughts, the two gold leaves are housed in a glass-fronted box. To ensure that the box does not carry a charge that will affect the leaves and ruin the readings, the box, which has a metal lining, is connected to earth while the electroscope is in use. Then, if the box

becomes positively charged, negative electrons flow from earth to make up the deficiency. Alternatively, if it becomes negatively charged, the extra electrons flow back to earth. So that the box can be kept closed when it is in use, the charge is conducted on to the gold leaves from outside. Above is a brass knob or disc joined to a thick brass rod leading into the box. The gold leaves are fixed to the end of this rod. Charge is put on the brass disc and conducted down the rod on to the gold leaves: gold is chosen because it can be beaten into

BRASS DISC

INSULATOR PLUG

GOLD LEAF

TERMINAL TO EARTH

LEAVES VIEWED THROUGH MICROSCOPE

Modified gold leaf electroscope for use with radio-active material.

IONIZED AIR CONDUCTS CHARGE FROM LEAF

RADIOACTIVE MATERIAL

there are equal numbers of positive and negative charges. When the negatively charged glass is brought near, the negative charges on the brass disc are repelled and move out of the way down to the gold leaves which as they are now negatively charged repel each other. The effect is only temporary, for when the charged body is taken away, the charges rearrange themselves and the leaves collapse. It can be made permanent by touching the brass disc with a finger while the rod is in position. This conducts away the negative charges from the disc, leaving the leaves still charged.

Lord Rutherford

very thin, light leaves which are capable of movement. Alloy leaves can also be used. To ensure that the charge does pass on to the leaves and not leak away on to the box, the brass rod is insulated by a plug of sulphur or ebonite or polythene.

There are two ways in which a gold leaf electroscope can be charged, resulting in the separation of its leaves. The charge can be put on by *contact* with a charged body or by *induction* where the charged body is brought near, but does not actually touch, the brass disc. When it is being charged by *contact* with a negatively charged body, negative charge flows across from the body on to the brass disc. Some is conducted down the brass rod on to the leaves which as they are both now negatively charged, repel each other, and separate. They remain separated when the charged body is taken away, showing that a charge has in fact been passed across. Touching the disc with a finger collapses the leaves when each experiment is finished. With *induction* no charge passes across. The brass parts and collapsed gold leaves have no overall charge, *i.e.*

96

To tell whether a charge is positive or negative.

First the brass disc is flicked with a piece of fur to make the gold leaves negatively charged. The fur is removed. The object under test is brought close to the brass disc. If it is positively charged, some negative charge is attracted up from the leaves. As their charge is lessened the leaves collapse slightly. This also happens with neutral bodies. If the object carries negative charge, negative charges are repelled from the brass disc down into the leaves which on account of their increased charge move further apart. Increased divergence is the only true test.

When two substances become charged by rubbing against each other, the charges are of the same size and opposite sign. The type of charge can be tested in the manner already described. When both substances are brought up to an uncharged electroscope, there is no divergence of the leaves, showing that jointly they have no effect. The positive charge is the same size as the negative.

A modified gold leaf electroscope was used by Lord Rutherford for his experiments using radioactive materials. The radioactive material was placed on a shelf under the gold leaf. Fast moving particles ejected from it ionized the surrounding air making it conducting so that the charges on the leaves leaked away and the divergence decreased. Rutherford observed the divergence with a microscope.

Some substances are insulators, others conductors. The gold leaf electroscope can be used to decide in which category a substance belongs. The electroscope is once more charged. The leaves stand apart. When a piece of sulphur is brought into contact with the brass disc, the leaves remain exactly as they are. The

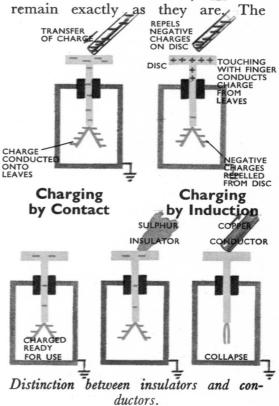

Charging by Contact   **Charging by Induction**

Distinction between insulators and conductors.

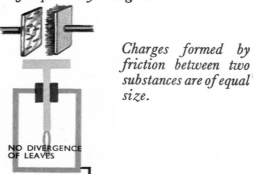

When glass and fur are rubbed together they become charged. Negatively charged electrons are rubbed on to the glass leaving the fur positively charged.

Charges formed by friction between two substances are of equal size.

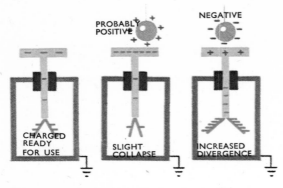

To test whether a charge is positive or negative.

charge has not been conducted away by the sulphur, which is an insulator. If, on the other hand, a piece of copper wire is tested, there is an immediate collapse of the leaves because the copper has conducted their charge away. Metals, water, and the human body are conductors. Rubber, silk, glass, amber and ebonite are examples of insulators. Some substances are partial insulators. Here the charge leaks away slowly.

FARADAY'S ICE PAIL EXPERIMENT

'No electrostatic field can exist inside a closed conducting vessel', was the conclusion Michael Faraday reached after he had been experimenting with electric fields around objects charged with static electricity. His 'closed conducting vessel' was a metal ice-pail. He had charged the pail with static electricity, knowing that static electric charges can 'act at a distance' on other electric charges, and make them experience an electrostatic force. An electrostatic 'field' is the name given to a region where this kind of force acts. Using a goldleaf electroscope, an instrument which can detect electrostatic forces, Faraday showed that there certainly were electrostatic forces acting *outside* the ice-pail. *Inside* the pail he could detect no force at all. So there could not possibly be any field there.

Faraday's conclusion is important to anyone who wants to protect something from electric fields – simply pop it inside a closed conducting vessel, like an ice-pail. This technique is widely used in electronic circuits, although the devices to 'shield' or 'screen' do not look very much like ice-pails. The screening in coaxial cable

leading to a television set, for example, is provided by the 'earthed' wire, wrapped around the other wires (and insulated from them). It prevents the cable from picking up stray fields. The fields are caused by electromagnetic waves – radio waves – which are a combination of disturbances of electric and magnetic fields. When the wave strikes a piece of conducting metal, electric currents are induced to flow to and fro in the metal. If the fields could reach the inner wires of the cable, currents would be induced in them, and the cable would be acting as an aerial. It would pick up mainly unwanted signals, which produce un-

Faraday's ice pail experiment which proves that the charge on a hollow conductor is situated on the outside.

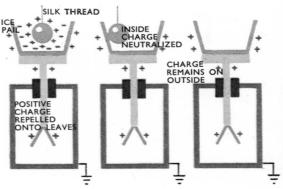

98

INSULATOR   EARTHED SCREENING   INSULATOR
                   LEAD

The outer network of wires acts like a 'closed conducting vessel'. It 'screens' the inner leads of the coaxial cable.

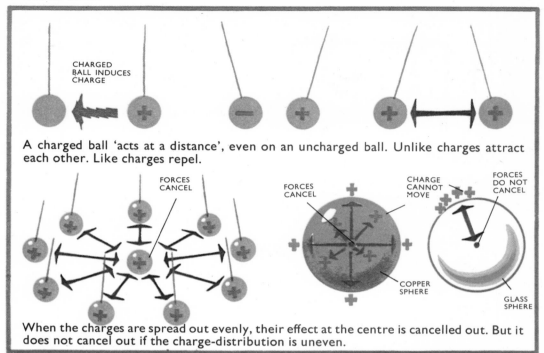

CHARGED BALL INDUCES CHARGE

A charged ball 'acts at a distance', even on an uncharged ball. Unlike charges attract each other. Like charges repel.

FORCES CANCEL

FORCES CANCEL

CHARGE CANNOT MOVE

FORCES DO NOT CANCEL

COPPER SPHERE

GLASS SPHERE

When the charges are spread out evenly, their effect at the centre is cancelled out. But it does not cancel out if the charge-distribution is uneven.

pleasant noise or 'hum' in the set. Currents are induced to flow to and fro in the outer earthed lead of the cable, but they flow harmlessly away to Earth. The important leads inside are free from disturbance. No electric field has been allowed to get *inside* the screening cylinder of wire.

There is no point in putting something inside an ice-pail if the fields are actually wanted. It is no use putting an aerial inside a closed conducting vessel and expecting it to pick up electro-magnetic waves. The aerials of small transistor radio sets are usually rods inside the set. If the set is put inside a car, with no special car aerial, it will probably not pick up a signal. The metal body of the car acts like an ice-pail, keeping the fields outside it and screening the set. However, signals may be detected if the transistor set is lifted up to be on the same level as the windows. Glass is not an electrical conductor, so it does not screen the signal from the aerial.

This demonstrates that good screen-ers must also be good conductors of electricity. There is no field inside because charges on the outside are completely free to arrange themselves in a particular way. Electrons in an electrical conductor are only loosely bound to their parent atoms. Under the influence of an electrostatic field, they are free to move around, and they do move, for the presence of an electro-static field implies that there are electrostatic *forces* there. Electrostatic forces act on electric charges, and move them.

For example, if a charge is put on the outside of an absolutely perfect hollow copper sphere, electrostatic forces act between all the individual charges. As they are either all positive charges or all negative charges, they repel each other, and move as far away from each other as possible. On a perfect sphere this means that they become distributed evenly over the outside of the whole surface.

Although the charges are on the outside, each contributes, by its 'action at a distance', to the field inside the sphere. The total effect can be found by adding up individual contributions but they are all acting in different directions, tending to cancel each other out. The net result is that there is no field in the centre at all. In fact, there is 'no field' at every single point inside the sphere.

Once charges are put on an electrical *insulator*, like glass, they cannot redistribute themselves. They are fixed. Charges are unbalanced outside, so the field *inside* is unbalanced, and is not cancelled out. So there is an electrostatic field inside a dry, hollow charged glass ball.

CAPACITORS

All matter contains positively and negatively charged particles. The positive particles, situated in the cores (nuclei) of atoms, are relatively heavy and, in solids, difficult to move. However, the negative charges, or electrons, are far smaller and easier to move. In a conducting metal, such as copper, they are very loosely bound to the nuclei, and can be made to drift through the metal if acted on by an electrical potential, or voltage.

What happens if the copper wire is then cut? Electrons cannot pile up indefinitely on one side of the gap. They can congregate until the repulsive forces between them (like electric charges repel) are equal to the force provided by the battery. Then the movement stops. One side of the gap has become negatively charged – an excess of electrons; and the other side positively charged – a lack of electrons. The field between the two sides (unlike charges, so an attractive field) holds the electric charges in place.

The battery can hold only a few electrons, make a small electric field

Each nucleus has a particular place in the metal – in the diagrams symbolised by a cup. It can roll around the bottom of the cup, but a tremendously large force would be needed to move the heavy particle from one cup to another. Electrons are loosely bound to the nuclei.

In a completed electrical circuit – a wire connected across the terminals of an ordinary battery – electrons can flow round the whole circuit, through the battery, where they are given energy to send them round again.

EACH FIXED UNIT OF CHARGE HAS A NEGATIVE CHARGE LOOSELY BOUND TO IT

When there is a gap in the wire, electron movement stops. A field is set up between the positive charges on one side, and the negative charges on the other. The amount of positive charge is equal to the amount of negative charge. The field holds the charges in place.

POSITIVE CHARGES PILE UP ON POSITIVE PLATE

ELECTRONS PILE UP ON NEGATIVE PLATE

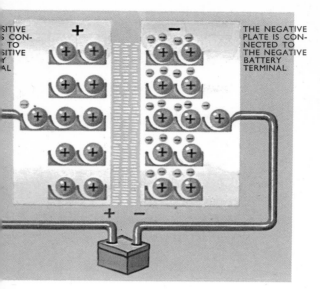

THE NEGATIVE
PLATE IS CON-
NECTED TO
THE NEGATIVE
BATTERY TERMINAL

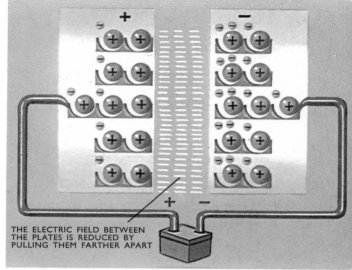

THE ELECTRIC FIELD BETWEEN
THE PLATES IS REDUCED BY
PULLING THEM FARTHER APART

The wire can hold a far greater charge if its area of cross-section is increased. Although there are a lot more electrons clustered together on the negative side, they will be spread over a larger area. The capacity increases.

The attractive field between the positive and negative sides holds the charges in place. If the distance between sides (or plates) is increased, one side will influence the other less. Less charge can be held in place – the capacity decreases.

in the gap and hold a small amount of charge if the wire is thin. Electrons huddled together in the same end of the wire repel each other very strongly because they are so close together. The wire can hold a far greater charge if its area of cross-section is increased, because the electrons are spread out over a larger area, and the repulsive forces tending to push them away from the gap will be less. When the two ends of the wire are pulled a greater distance apart, the field is reduced, and the charge held decreases.

Thus two pieces of conducting material, facing each other, have a certain capacity for holding electric charge. The two metal surfaces are called *plates* and their capacity is increased by increasing their area, and decreased by pulling them farther apart. The device is called, for obvious reasons, a *capacitor*, or alternatively, a *condenser*, because it condenses (assembles) together electric charges.

At the instant when a battery is connected across a capacitor (or condenser) a temporary, or *transient* current flows in the circuit. The voltage difference (difference in electrical potential) between the two capacitor plates gradually increases to a maximum – in this case the voltage difference supplied by the battery. The amount of charge stored by the capacitor depends directly on its capacitance and on the voltage connected across it. The diagrams show how a capacitor is charged and then discharged by connecting the battery terminals the opposite way round. When this is done very quickly, it is similar to an alternating, to-and-fro current. If one complete cycle of the alternating current takes less time than the time to completely charge the capacitor, the capacitor continually charges and discharges and the flow of current through it is continuous. Thus while the capacitor has an infinitely large resistance to

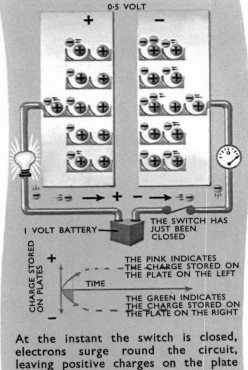

0·5 VOLT

+   −

THE SWITCH HAS JUST BEEN CLOSED

I VOLT BATTERY

CHARGE STORED ON PLATES

+

−

TIME

THE PINK INDICATES THE CHARGE STORED ON THE PLATE ON THE LEFT

THE GREEN INDICATES THE CHARGE STORED ON THE PLATE ON THE RIGHT

At the instant the switch is closed, electrons surge round the circuit, leaving positive charges on the plate connected to the positive battery terminal. The negative electron charge is stored on the negative plate and a voltage difference, or difference in electric potential, is built up between the plates.

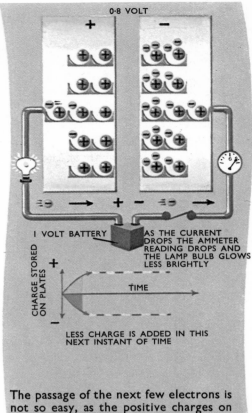

0·8 VOLT

+   −

AS THE CURRENT DROPS THE AMMETER READING DROPS AND THE LAMP BULB GLOWS LESS BRIGHTLY

I VOLT BATTERY

CHARGE STORED ON PLATES

+

−

TIME

LESS CHARGE IS ADDED IN THIS NEXT INSTANT OF TIME

The passage of the next few electrons is not so easy, as the positive charges on the positive plate tend to hold electrons back, while the negative charges on the negative plate tend to push them back.

direct current – it will allow no current to pass through at all after the initial charging – it will let a rapidly changing alternating current pass through it fairly easily.

Capacitor circuits can be thought of as tubes (the connecting wires) with a rubber bag tied on at each end (the plates of the capacitor).

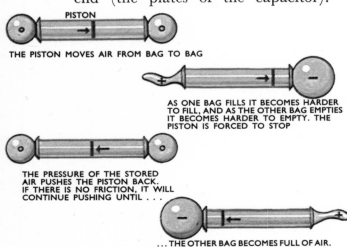

PISTON

THE PISTON MOVES AIR FROM BAG TO BAG

− AS ONE BAG FILLS IT BECOMES HARDER TO FILL, AND AS THE OTHER BAG EMPTIES IT BECOMES HARDER TO EMPTY. THE PISTON IS FORCED TO STOP

THE PRESSURE OF THE STORED AIR PUSHES THE PISTON BACK. IF THERE IS NO FRICTION, IT WILL CONTINUE PUSHING UNTIL . . .

. . . THE OTHER BAG BECOMES FULL OF AIR. THE PISTON STOPS AND IS PUSHED BACK AGAIN. IF THERE IS NO FRICTION THE MOVEMENT CONTINUES INDEFINITELY

The electric current can be represented by a flow of air from one bag to the other through the pipe. The force needed to push the air from bag to bag (in the circuit the force provided by the battery, or alternating current supply) is given by a piston. As the piston moves from side to side it pushes the air in the tube to-and-fro, to form an alternating current of air.

The bags store air, as the capacitor plates store electrons. A full bag is equivalent to a capacitor plate full to capacity of electrons. The fuller the bag, the more difficult it is to push more air into it, while the emptier the bag gets, the more it resists further emptying. As the piston is moved to the extreme right or left of the tube, it is forced to stop by the high pressure in the negative bag

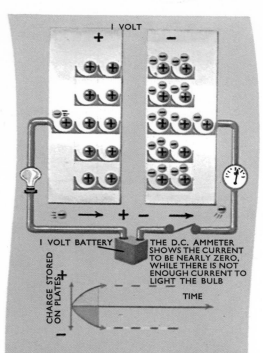

The last few electrons are transferred very slowly, and the current in the circuit dwindles to nothing. The voltage (difference in electric potential caused by the accumulation of charge) is now 1 volt, the voltage supplied by the battery.

pushing it back, and the near vacuum in the other bag sucking it back.

This resistance which the capacitor plates give to the addition of more electrons is not the usual kind of electrical resistance, where electrons have to batter their way through the material, losing energy each time they bump into another particle. In a resistance the energy needed to force electrons through is converted into heat, and usually wasted. But capacitors *store* energy given them by the battery or alternating current supply. If the current is switched to the opposite direction, electrons will rush to the other plate and transfer energy from one plate to another, *without losing it*. The resistance which they offer to the flow of current is called *reactance*.

It is easiest to move the piston when the pressure in the two bags is about equal. But when there is a *difference* in pressure between the two bags, less air can move. When the

The battery terminals are suddenly switched round. Electrons can now surge round the circuit in the opposite direction, discharging and recharging the plates, making the original positive plate negative, and *vice versa*.

103

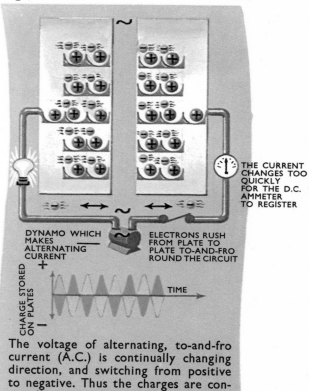

The voltage of alternating, to-and-fro current (A.C.) is continually changing direction, and switching from positive to negative. Thus the charges are continually moving from one plate to the other around the circuit (but not, of course, across the air gap between the plates).

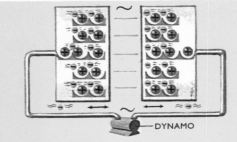

The reactance of a capacitor depends on its capacitance.

Double the capacitance (halve distance of plates apart): halve reactance.

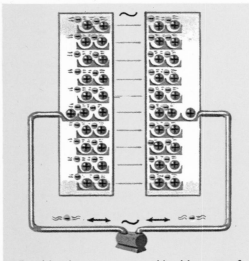

Double the capacitance (double area of plates): halve reactance.

two capacitor plates. This is greatest when there is least current charging the capacitor.

The reactance of a capacitor depends on two things—its capacitance, which is a measure of the amount of charge it is capable of storing, and the speed with which the direction of the current varies—in other words the *frequency* of an alternating current. How does the reactance vary with capacitance and frequency? Take, for example, a large capacitor. This has a large surface area, and the distance between the plates is small. Electrons can flow more easily onto the plates because the repulsive forces preventing them from getting there will be smaller (these increase the closer the electrons are huddled together). Once electrons are on the plate they are held in place by the strong electric field of attraction from the positive plate. So the larger the capacitor, the smaller its reactance. A larger bag will be easier to fill (with the same amount of air) than a smaller bag.

The quicker the direction of the alternating to-and-fro current changes, the easier it is for electrons to flow, because a large stockpile of electrons is not given chance to accumulate and repel further electrons. In the tube and bags the direction changes so quickly that the piston oscillates about the centre of the tube, only a short distance away from it, in the region where the air is easiest to move. Thus, as the frequency of an alternating current increases, the reactance of a capacitor decreases.

pressure difference is at a maximum, the movement of air is at a minimum (i.e. none at all). The pressure difference between the two bags is equivalent to the difference in electric 'pressure', or voltage, between the

In a circuit containing just resistance, as the voltage across the resistance increases, so does the current.

In a circuit containing capacitance, as the voltage across the capacitor increases, the current decreases.

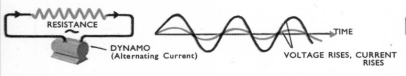

CHAPTER TWENTY-FOUR

Capacitors in Series and Parallel

IF electrical capacitors are connected side-by-side (in *parallel*), their total capacitance is the sum of all the individual capacitances. Electric currents cannot actually flow *through* a capacitor, because the capacitor is a gap in an electric circuit. However, electric charge can accumulate on the large areas (the plates) on either side of the gap. The bigger the area of the plates, the bigger the *capacitance*. More charge can accumulate there.

The *capacitance* of a capacitor is also a measure of its ability to pass on alternating electric currents. Charge can flow, to-and-fro, on to one of the plates, attracting a charge of opposite sign, the flow to-and-fro, on to the other plate.

Connecting capacitors in parallel simply makes a bigger area on either side of the gap. If three capacitors, C_1, C_2 and C_3 are connected in parallel,

then $C_{TOTAL} = C_1 + C_2 + C_3$

But if the string of capacitors is connected one after another (in *series*) the total capacitance drops. It becomes less than the capacitance of any

one of the individual capacitors. Electrical charges have to be attracted across several circuit gaps, instead of just one gap in one capacitor. Extra gaps make the transfer more difficult – in fact the capacitance of a capacitor is *inversely proportional* to the gap size. Inversely proportional means that when the gap size *increases*, the capacitance *decreases*.

It can be written in another way:

Capacitance is proportional to $\dfrac{1}{\text{gap size}}$,

or, the other way around:

$\dfrac{1}{\text{capacitance}}$ is proportional to gap size

When capacitors are connected in series, it is their gap sizes which are added together. The total gap size is:

Gap $_{TOTAL}$ = Gap$_1$ + Gap$_2$ + Gap$_3$

The total capacitance is the *inverse* of this, or: $\dfrac{1}{C_{TOTAL}} = \dfrac{1}{C_1} + \dfrac{1}{C_2} + \dfrac{1}{C_3}$

This is the rule for calculating capacitance in series.

The formulae for capacitors in series and parallel are similar to the formulae for resistors in parallel and series.

Resistors in Series:

$R_{TOTAL} = R_1 + R_2 + R_3$

$R_1 \qquad R_2 \qquad R_3$

Resistors in parallel –

$\dfrac{1}{R_{TOTAL}} = \dfrac{1}{R_1} + \dfrac{1}{R_2} + \dfrac{1}{R_3}$

R_1
R_2
R_3

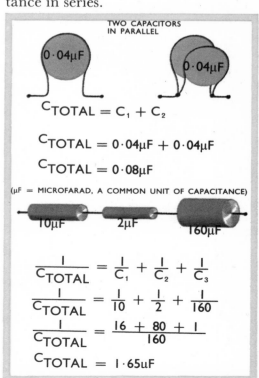

TWO CAPACITORS IN PARALLEL

0·04μF   0·04μF

$C_{TOTAL} = C_1 + C_2$

$C_{TOTAL} = 0\cdot04μF + 0\cdot04μF$

$C_{TOTAL} = 0\cdot08μF$

(μF = MICROFARAD, A COMMON UNIT OF CAPACITANCE)

10μF   2μF   160μF

$\dfrac{1}{C_{TOTAL}} = \dfrac{1}{C_1} + \dfrac{1}{C_2} + \dfrac{1}{C_3}$

$\dfrac{1}{C_{TOTAL}} = \dfrac{1}{10} + \dfrac{1}{2} + \dfrac{1}{160}$

$\dfrac{1}{C_{TOTAL}} = \dfrac{16 + 80 + 1}{160}$

$C_{TOTAL} = 1\cdot65uF$

The basic unit of capacitance is an enormous unit called the *farad*. It is equal to the quantity of electric charge (in coulombs = amps x time) needed to raise the electrical potential (or voltage) of the capacitor by one volt. This unit is so excessively large that even the capacitance of the Earth is less than a thousandth of a farad. For practical purposes microfarads (μF) – a millionth of a farad – and pica-farads (pF) – a millionth of a millionth of a farad – are used.

CHAPTER TWENTY-FIVE

Capacitance and the Farad

THE ability of a body to store electric charges on its surface is known as its *capacitance*. The storage of charge can be compared with the storage of water in a container. The more liquid stored, the higher the pressure at the base of the container. Similarly, the more charge on a surface, the higher the electric *potential*.

However, electrical capacitance differs from the water capacity of a tank, in that it takes account of the level or *pressure* of the charge, as well as of the *quantity* of charge. (A tall thin vessel, holding one gallon when full, has just the same capacity as a short, squat one which also holds one gallon when full. The levels will be different, though.)

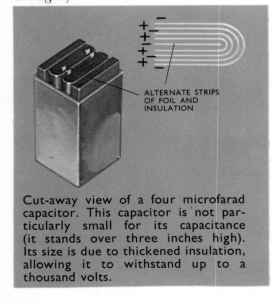

ALTERNATE STRIPS OF FOIL AND INSULATION

Cut-away view of a four microfarad capacitor. This capacitor is not particularly small for its capacitance (it stands over three inches high). Its size is due to thickened insulation, allowing it to withstand up to a thousand volts.

If a current of one ampere (amp) is allowed to flow through a circuit for one second, the total quantity of charge passed is one *coulomb*. This may not seem a very large quantity in terms of current electricity, but if we tried to store it on a metal sphere, six feet in diameter, the sphere would be raised to a potential of 9,000 million volts. In fact it is impossible to store such a large charge, because the voltage is far too high, and a breakdown of the insulation of the surrounding air would occur long before this potential could be reached. (This is rather like trying to get several thousand gallons into a very long, vertical glass tube, an inch in diameter. The level would rise to several miles, producing a pressure at the bottom too great for the tube to withstand.)

Another way of saying that the potential would rise to 9000 million volts is to say that the ball has a capacity of one nine-thousandth of a millionth of a *farad*. A capacity of one farad holds a charge of one coulomb at a potential of one volt. In practice it is a very large unit indeed. It would need 9000 million six-foot spheres to give a one farad capacity – or a single sphere ten million miles across. This would be much larger than the Earth itself – in fact the Earth's capacity is only about one thousandth of a farad.

The potential of the charged surface

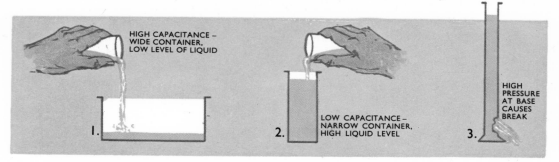

1. HIGH CAPACITANCE – WIDE CONTAINER, LOW LEVEL OF LIQUID

2. LOW CAPACITANCE – NARROW CONTAINER, HIGH LIQUID LEVEL

3. HIGH PRESSURE AT BASE CAUSES BREAK

arises because like charges repel each other, and so a state of tension is set up. The more charges there are on a surface, the closer they are to each other and the greater is the tension. If the charge is continually increased, a stage is eventually reached where the tension becomes so high that charges begin to 'jump off' the surface – the air-resistance breaks down.

Capacitors (also called condensers) are used in radio and electronics. They store the charge not on metal spheres but on plates or foils. In its simplest form a capacitor has two plates, set face to face with a small gap separating them. One plate becomes positive and the other negative, and the charges are held in position by the electric field between the plates.

Plate capacitors have a much greater capacitance than metal spheres. One small enough to fit into

The storage of electric charge can be compared with the storage of water in a container. (1) A high capacitance can store charge (water) at a low electrical potential. (2) The same amount of charge is stored at higher potential in a low capacitance. (3) When the potential is too high, the insulation breaks down.

the hand may be equivalent to a sphere several miles across. Typical values range from a millionth-millionth of a farad (a *pica farad*) to about one tenth of a thousandth of a farad. (The latter is equivalent to a four hundred mile sphere.)

These very large capacitors can be used to deliver enormous currents, i.e. at large rates of discharge – but only for a very brief period. As stores of energy they are used to give high voltage pulses in atomic research, and to give the discharge currents for flash photography.

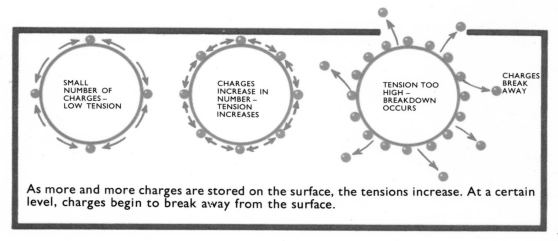

SMALL NUMBER OF CHARGES – LOW TENSION

CHARGES INCREASE IN NUMBER – TENSION INCREASES

TENSION TOO HIGH – BREAKDOWN OCCURS

CHARGES BREAK AWAY

As more and more charges are stored on the surface, the tensions increase. At a certain level, charges begin to break away from the surface.

CHAPTER TWENTY-SIX

Capacitors – The Dielectric

IN its simplest form, a capacitor is a pair of metal plates, separated from each other by a gap. In the kind of capacitor normally found attached to the tuning knob of a radio receiver there are a number of parallel plates which can be moved so that they intermesh with one another.

The gap between the plates is important because it helps to store the electric charge on the capacitor plates. In most capacitors the gap is filled with an electrical insulator – air (as in the radio tuning capacitor), paper, mica, or oiled paper. The filling is called the *dielectric*.

Because the dielectric is an electrical insulator, it does not let electric current pass *directly* through it. But it behaves as if it allows through alternating currents, where the electric charge surging on to the plates changes direction rapidly. Negative charges rush first to one plate, then to the other, going around the rest of the circuit and not across the dielectric.

The valves or transistors in radio circuits are usually supplied with direct current, while the radio signal itself is an alternating current. Capacitors are included to make sure that the two different types of current do not mix with each other. The capacitor lets through alternating currents, but not direct currents. The energy of the alternating current is temporarily stored when the charges surge on to the plates, and it is released when they surge off again.

Like all matter, the dielectric is made up of atoms. A positively charged part in the middle of the atom, the *nucleus*, is surrounded by negative charges, *electrons*. In an electrical insulator, electrons are firmly bound to the nuclei. Electrons cannot be separated from nuclei, unless they are subjected to very strong electrostatic forces. However they can be displaced slightly so that one side of the atom is slightly positive and the other side is slightly negative.

Near the negatively-charged plate of the capacitor the positive nuclei are pulled slightly towards the plate, and the negative electrons are pushed slightly away. The opposite happens near the positive plate. Energy is used in shifting them, so while they are displaced, dielectric atoms are in fact storing energy. The energy will be released when the charge on the plates collapses.

The capacitor stores electric charge, but it also stores energy. Both really come to the same thing.

Some materials are better dielectrics than others. Solid substances, for example, have more atoms packed into a small space, so there are more atoms available to store energy. Dielectric properties also depend on the size, shape and arrangement of atoms and molecules in the substance. When the voltage across the dielectric becomes too high, its insulating properties may break down.

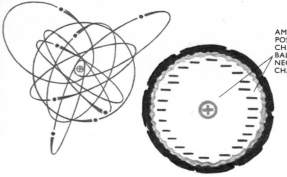

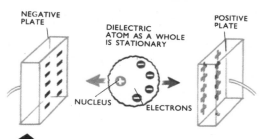

AMOUNT OF POSITIVE CHARGE BALANCES NEGATIVE CHARGES

The positively charged nucleus of an atom is surrounded by negatively-charged electrons. The amount of positive charge just balances the amount of negative charge, so the atom is electrically neutral.

NEGATIVE PLATE

DIELECTRIC ATOM AS A WHOLE IS STATIONARY

POSITIVE PLATE

NUCLEUS   ELECTRONS

NEGATIVE PLATE

POSITIVE PLATE

EXTRA CHARGE INDUCED

EXTRA CHARGE INDUCED

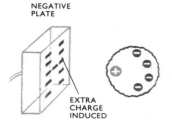

▲

Charges on the capacitor plates displace the charges of the atom. The charged atom attracts (induces) more charges on the plates.

The dielectric increases the charges on the plates because the total charge includes the induced charges. It therefore increases the capacitance of the capacitor.

▼

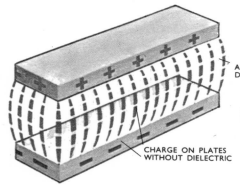

AIR DIELECTRIC

CHARGE ON PLATES WITHOUT DIELECTRIC

TUNING CAPACITOR

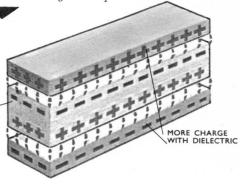

SOLID DIELECTRIC

MORE CHARGE WITH DIELECTRIC

Air and waxed paper are commonly-used dielectrics.

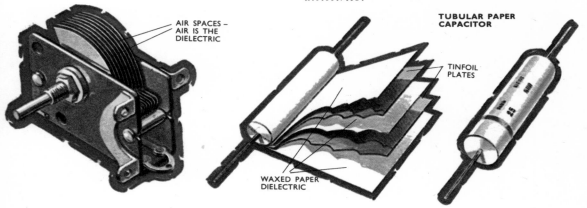

AIR SPACES – AIR IS THE DIELECTRIC

TUBULAR PAPER CAPACITOR

TINFOIL PLATES

WAXED PAPER DIELECTRIC

109

CHAPTER TWENTY-SEVEN

Electrolytic Capacitors

CAPACITORS in electronic circuits are used as temporary storers of electric charge. The capacitor consists of two metal plates (the *electrodes*) separated by an electrical insulator (the *dielectric*). A special feature of electrolytic capacitors is that one of the plates is covered by an *electrolyte*, an ionic substance which conducts electricity. For their size, electrolytic capacitors have a very large capacitance, or ability to store electric charge.

The charge is stored on the electrodes themselves, and the dielectric between the electrodes. Although the atoms in the dielectric cannot be moved bodily by the electric field between the electrodes, positively charged nuclei can be shifted slightly towards the negative electrode and negatively charged electrons can be shifted slightly towards the positive electrode. While they are shifted, they are, in effect, storing charge and in-creasing the amount of charge held on the electrodes.

A thin piece of dielectric is better than a thick piece. The electric *field* between the electrodes is higher when they are closer together since the charge on one plate can *induce* a larger charge on the other plate.

In electrolytic capacitors, the dielectric is very thin indeed. It is a film of aluminium oxide formed directly (*by electrolysis*) on one of the aluminium electrodes. This very thin film gives the electrolytic capacitor its very high capacitance. However, to make full use of the very thin dielectric, it must be in good electrical contact with both electrodes. This is achieved by filling in the space between the oxidized electrode (the positive electrode) and the other electrode with the electrolyte. Electric current can flow through the electrolyte because it contains free positively and negatively charged particles, or *ions*.

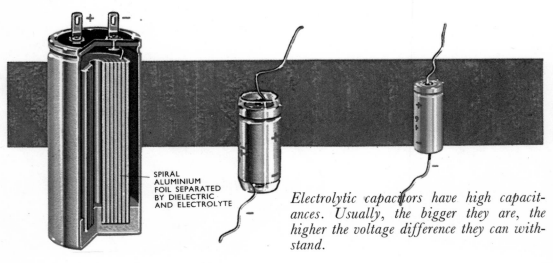

SPIRAL
ALUMINIUM
FOIL SEPARATED
BY DIELECTRIC
AND ELECTROLYTE

Electrolytic capacitors have high capacitances. Usually, the bigger they are, the higher the voltage difference they can withstand.

There are disadvantages in having a very thin dielectric. It does not insulate electrode from electrode if the voltage difference across the plates is too high. Most small electrolytic capacitors can withstand a voltage difference between electrodes of only a few volts, but this is quite adequate for capacitors in transistor radio sets, where voltage differences are never more than a few volts. Capacitors to withstand higher voltages can be made, but they are inevitably larger.

Most electrolytic capacitors can be connected into a circuit only one way round. The electrode with the aluminium oxide layer must be positive. If it is connected the other way around the oxide will decompose.

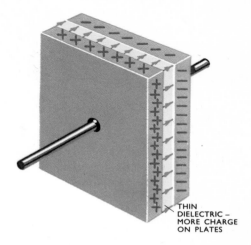

THIN DIELECTRIC – MORE CHARGE ON PLATES

The capacitance of an electrolytic capacitor is high because the dielectric is thin.

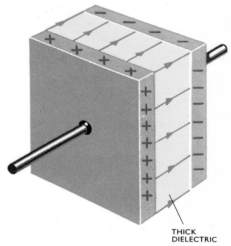

THICK DIELECTRIC

A thick dielectric leads to low electric field and low capacitance. Electrolytic capacitors have very thin dielectrics. This is the reason for their high capacitance.

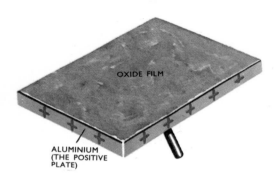

OXIDE FILM

ALUMINIUM (THE POSITIVE PLATE)

DIAGRAM OF A CROSS-SECTION OF AN ELECTROLYTIC CAPACITOR

NEGATIVE ALUMINIUM ELECTRODE

ELECTROLYTE

DIELECTRIC

Top: A thin film of oxide is formed on the positive electrode. Above: the space between film and negative electrode is filled with electrolyte.

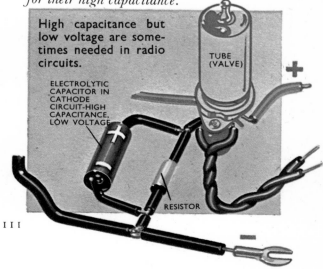

High capacitance but low voltage are sometimes needed in radio circuits.

TUBE (VALVE)

ELECTROLYTIC CAPACITOR IN CATHODE CIRCUIT-HIGH CAPACITANCE, LOW VOLTAGE

RESISTOR

A chimney without a lightning conductor. Lightning has blasted a path down the chimney in its attempt to reach the ground.

A 'single' flash of lightning, analysed by a moving camera into a number of successive flashes.

The layer of the charge on the underside of a thundercloud induces a positive charge on the surface of the earth beneath. This charge accumulates on high objects and an electric 'wind' leaks off from the spike of the lightning conductor. Sudden local accumulations of charge on the cloud are forced down to meet the electric 'wind'.

CHAPTER TWENTY-EIGHT

Lightning Conductors

LIGHTNING is always dangerous and unpredictable, but by understanding what lightning really is and how it happens, much of the damage it used to cause can now be prevented.

Lightning is simply the spark produced when electrical charges within a cloud suddenly flow from cloud to cloud or from cloud to earth. Most of the charge is 'manufactured' inside the thunder cloud, where turbulent air currents moving up and down at terrific speed toss raindrops and ice crystals about. As they rub violently together, friction causes the transfer of electric charges (electrons) from one particle to another. Somehow (the actual mechanism of the process is still not fully understood) charges of *one* type, positive or negative, but usually negative, accumulate on the underside of the cloud.

The negative charge on the cloud means that the cloud is at a negative voltage (electric potential) relative to the earth. The electric potential tends to push the electric charges towards the earth, but the air in between is normally a bad conductor of electricity and an enormous voltage (of the order of millions of volts) between cloud and earth is needed before a spark can flow between them.

The passage of a spark is made easier by the fact that the earth underneath the cloud becomes charged – positively charged if the cloud is negatively charged – during a thunderstorm. The process which brings this about is called *electrostatic induction*.

Negative electric charges repel other negative charges, so the cloud repels negative charges (electrons) in the surface of the earth beneath it. The movement of electrons may

In a thunderstorm the spike of a lightning conductor becomes highly charged (see inset).

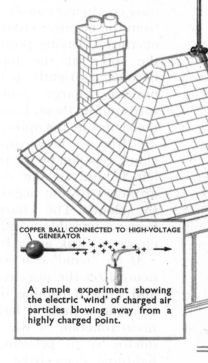

COPPER BALL CONNECTED TO HIGH-VOLTAGE GENERATOR

A simple experiment showing the electric 'wind' of charged air particles blowing away from a highly charged point.

be only slight because much of the earth is made from insulating material. But it leaves a positive charge (called an *induced* charge) on the surface of the earth directly underneath the thundercloud, equal to the negative charge on the thundercloud. As the cloud moves, so the area of positive charge underneath it moves. Cloud and earth are like the two plates of a capacitor, loaded with electric charge, but unable to discharge it because of the insulating layer of air in between.

A lightning conductor is a sharply pointed rod of conducting metal, attached to the highest point of a building and joined by a thick copper cable to a copper plate buried in the ground. The electrons in the lightning conductor can easily move away from the negative charge in the cloud overhead, leaving positive charges in the spike at the top. These will become so tightly packed that the positive charge ionizes the air surrounding them. Unlike the charged molecules in the spike, air molecules are free to move up towards the cloud, repelled by the positive charges left behind in the conductor, and attracted by the negative charges in the cloud. The charged molecules form an invisible 'wind' which allows charge to leak away from the earth.

If the 'wind' reaches the cloud, it neutralizes the negative charge there and stops it coming down from the cloud in a flash of lightning. So the main function of the lightning conductor is to prevent lightning. If lightning does strike, the conductor prevents it from doing harm. Sudden local accumulations of charge on the cloud become too great to be held back by the insulation of the air, and

a stream of electrons is directed towards the earth. The cloud first sends out a 'leader' stream, descending from the cloud in steps and branching as it tries to find the path offering it the least resistance. It tears apart the molecules in the air it passes through, ionizing them so that they can conduct following streams of electrons. This violent force excites the air, and makes it emit light. The spark we see is light emitted from the ionised air around the jagged path taken by the lightning. As the air is excited it expands explosively, and the noise of this explosion is called thunder.

Once the lightning has struck the earth it still tries to find the easiest path along which to travel. Often the lightning stream finds that the easiest thing to do is to rebound back up to the cloud, along the conducting path it has made for itself. During what appears to be a single flash the stream may pass many times backwards and forwards along this same path. All this happens in a fraction of a second.

Lightning will naturally travel towards any high object, a building, or a tree because electric charge tends to accumulate at the top of them. It will be even more strongly attracted towards the high, sharply-pointed metal spikes of a lightning conductor attached to the top of a high building because these will be more positively charged. The electric wind from the spikes may have already made a conducting path, reaching some way upwards to meet the spark coming down. And as the lightning conductor is connected by a conducting copper wire to a copper plate dug in the earth, the lightning striking the metal point will be discharged harmlessly to earth.

Further Methods of Producing Electricity

CHAPTER TWENTY-NINE

Electricity made by Chemical Means

THE electricity used in factories and in the home is supplied through cables from a generator in a power station. But electric current cannot be stored like water (for it is only the *movement* of electrons along the wire while the potential is operating at both ends) and it is not practical to carry a generator, which is driven by (say) a Diesel engine around with you in order to produce electricity for such things as flashlights. Some small, portable means of producing electricity is therefore needed. Cells and batteries (a series of cells) are small and easily carried. Electricity is produced in them by chemical means.

The Simple Electric Cell (the voltaic cell invented by Alessandro Volta)

When most metals are put into a tank of acid, they will be chemically attacked by the acid. If two plates of different metals (or a metal plate and a carbon plate) are put into a tank containing acid and water, the complicated chemical reactions that occur leave the metal atoms that the acid has attacked in the first plate with a surplus of electrons. A by-product of the chemical reaction is the release of hydrogen atoms that were originally in the acid and are now short of their electrons (in this state they are called hydrogen ions). *These drift towards the second plate, from which they take the electrons of which they are short. So the second plate has an overall deficiency of electrons – a positive charge. This difference in electric charge between the two plates is enough to cause a drift of electrons along a copper wire externally connecting the two – an electric current flowing through an electric circuit. There is one snag to this. The hydrogen atoms (now complete) attach themselves as a complete film over the second plate and very soon (a matter of seconds) prevent any more hydrogen ions reaching the plate to steal electrons. This is called* polarization. *In practical cells, therefore, an extra chemical is included that joins readily with the complete hydrogen atoms and takes them away from the plate. Also it is possible to replace the acid by a chemical such as ammonium chloride, much safer for people to carry.*

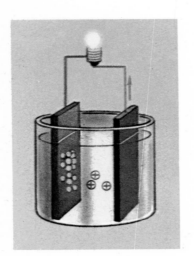

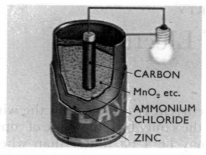

CARBON
MnO₂ etc.
AMMONIUM
CHLORIDE
ZINC

Storage Batteries or Accumulator

The simple voltaic cell and the dry cell are called primary or irreversible cells because the chemical reaction cannot be reversed and the materials used all over again. A secondary or reversible cell (e.g. a car battery) can be recharged and used again by passing a direct current of electricity in the reverse direction that the current flows in the cell. This completely reverses the chemical reaction that produced the current and so returns the chemicals to their previous state.

The lead accumulator or lead storage battery is an example of a secondary cell. It consists of two kinds of lead plates, which are, in fact, grids or gratings to increase the surface area in contact with the acid. The holes in one kind are filled with spongy lead and the other with lead peroxide. The all-lead plates (negative) correspond to the zinc casing of the dry cell and the lead peroxide plates (positive) correspond to the carbon rod.

A single cell of a storage battery is made up of a series of alternate negative (lead) and positive (lead peroxide) plates. The plates are immersed in a solution of sulphuric acid and distilled water.

Both the lead and the lead peroxide react with sulphuric acid to form lead sulphate. When both sets of plates are covered with a white deposit of lead sulphate the cell runs down because there is then no difference between the plates. The recharging current turns the lead sulphate back to lead on one plate and lead peroxide on the other. A complete battery consists of three or six cells connected up in an 'electrical tandem' arrangement, that adds together the e.m.f. of all the cells.

The Dry Cell

The dry cell consists of a zinc container (the negative 'plate' of the cell) inside which is a rod of carbon (positive 'plate') packed round with a moist mixture of carbon powder, manganese dioxide and ammonium chloride. The chemical reaction between the ammonium chloride and the zinc case puts a surplus of electrons onto the zinc, and leaves the carbon rod (which acts as the second 'plate') with a shortage of electrons.

When the circuit is broken the chemical reaction stops because the electrons released from the zinc atoms cannot escape along the wire to the carbon rod. This is why the light in a flashlight is extinguished when it is switched off. Switching it on again allows the electrons to escape from the zinc and flow to the carbon.

A flashlight battery can no longer work when all the ammonium chloride (the equivalent of the acid) has been used up. It then has to be thrown away as it is cheaper to make a new dry cell than to renew the parts.

CHAPTER THIRTY

Faraday's Laws of Electrolysis

CUTTING a wire in an electric circuit stops the flow of current because low voltage electricity can only jump a very small gap. The air between the ends of the wires is non-conducting and acts as an insulator, stopping the current from flowing. If the two ends are dipped in oil, still no current flows because oil, like air, is another insulator.

The current can be made to flow again by dipping the wire into a solution of a salt or an acid or an alkali. Molten salts also give the same results. Because they are capable of conducting electricity, all these liquids are known as *electrolytes*.

When an electric current flows along a piece of copper wire, it remains virtually unchanged. When the current is switched off, the wire is just the same. It is still made of copper. It may be a bit hotter than when it started out but certainly no chemical change has taken place.

However, chemical changes do take place when most liquids apart from mercury are made to conduct electricity. The changes take place at the *electrodes* (the bare wires dipping into the solution). Sometimes the negative electrode (*cathode*) grows fatter at the expense of the *anode*, (the positive electrode). The deposited layer of metal grows thicker and thicker as more electricity is passed. Bubbles of gases sometimes rise from the electrodes. When acidified water is electrolyzed, bubbles of hydrogen rise from the cathode and oxygen bubbles are

Michael Faraday

Quantity of electricity is measured in coulombs. When a current of 2 amperes flows for 5 seconds, 10 coulombs of electricity have passed.

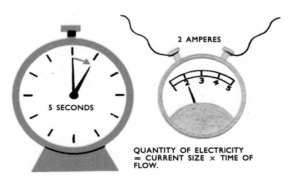

5 SECONDS

2 AMPERES

QUANTITY OF ELECTRICITY = CURRENT SIZE × TIME OF FLOW.

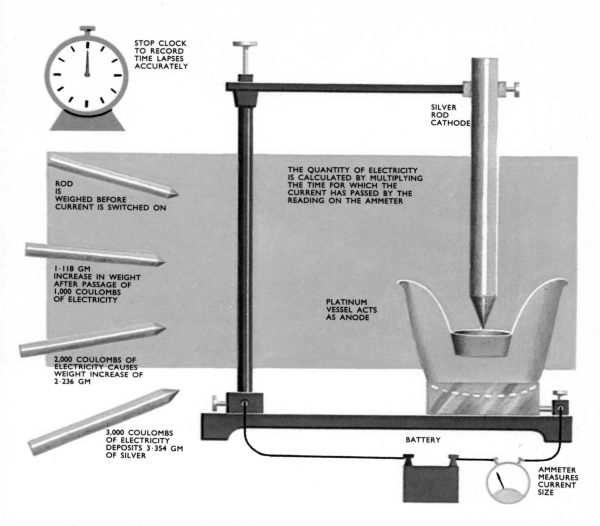

STOP CLOCK
TO RECORD
TIME LAPSES
ACCURATELY

SILVER
ROD
CATHODE

THE QUANTITY OF ELECTRICITY
IS CALCULATED BY MULTIPLYING
THE TIME FOR WHICH THE
CURRENT HAS PASSED BY THE
READING ON THE AMMETER

ROD
IS
WEIGHED BEFORE
CURRENT IS SWITCHED ON

1·118 GM
INCREASE IN WEIGHT
AFTER PASSAGE OF
1,000 COULOMBS
OF ELECTRICITY

PLATINUM
VESSEL ACTS
AS ANODE

2,000 COULOMBS OF
ELECTRICITY CAUSES
WEIGHT INCREASE OF
2·236 GM

3,000 COULOMBS
OF ELECTRICITY
DEPOSITS 3·354 GM
OF SILVER

BATTERY

AMMETER
MEASURES
CURRENT
SIZE

1·118 grams of silver are deposited on the cathode by the passage of 1,000 coulombs of electricity. 2,000 coulombs deposit twice as much silver and 3,000, three times as much. This is in accordance with Faraday's first law of electrolysis.

given off at the anode.

Faraday's laws do not predict what will happen when substances are electrolyzed. This is easy to discover by experiment. But they can be used to predict the *quantities* of substance liberated.

Faraday's first law of electrolysis states that *the weight of a substance liberated during electrolysis is proportional to the quantity of electricity passed.*

The quantity of electricity depends on two factors, the size of the current and the time for which it is passed. For example, in terms of quantity, a current of 1 ampere flowing for 10 minutes is the same as a 2 ampere current flowing for five minutes or even a 5 ampere current flowing for 2 minutes, and the same weight of copper would be deposited under all three conditions.

Just as weights are measured in grams, so current quantities are

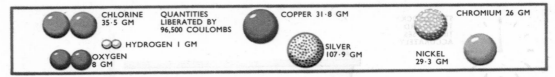

In electrolysis, the passage of 96,500 coulombs of electricity liberates an equivalent weight of substance. For example 96,500 coulombs of electricity liberates 8 grams of oxygen.

measured in *coulombs*. One coulomb is the quantity of electricity which passes when a current of one ampere flows for one second. If two amperes flow for 10 seconds, then 20 coulombs of electricity have passed. Quantity of electricity in coulombs = current × time.

If one gram of copper is deposited by a certain quantity of electricity, twice the quantity will deposit 2 grams and three times the quantity of electricity, 3 grams etc. This is another way of expressing Faraday's first law.

When acidified water undergoes electrolysis, it splits up into its component elements, hydrogen and oxygen. Bubbles of hydrogen escape from the cathode and oxygen from the anode. When all the gases escaping from each are collected, it is found that 8 grams of oxygen are given off for every gram of hydrogen liberated. The same quantity of electricity needed to release 8 grams of oxygen sets free 35·5 grams of chlorine when molten sodium chloride is electrolysed. 8, 1 and 35·5 grams are the *equilavent weights* of oxygen, hydrogen and chlorine.

The equivalent weight of any element can be calculated by looking up its atomic weight and dividing this by the valency. Oxygen has an atomic weight of 16 and a valency of 2. Consequently its equivalent weight is 8. Because chlorine has a valency of 1, the atomic weight and the equivalent weight are the same. Likewise for hydrogen.

It is quite reasonable that elements should be liberated in quantities proportional to their equivalent weights rather than their atomic weights. Two atoms of hydrogen can each ferry across a current electron. But because it is divalent, a single atom of oxygen can transport the same quantity of electricity. Therefore for every two atoms of hydrogen liberated there will be only one of oxygen and for every gram of hydrogen liberated, 8 grams of oxygen will be given off.

So the same quantity of electricity is required to release equivalent weights of any element. By experiment, this value has proved to be 96,500 coulombs. The passage of 96,500 coulombs of electricity will liberate 1 gram of hydrogen, 8 of oxygen, or 35·5 grams of chlorine.

This fact together with the two laws can be used to work out actual weights of substance liberated in electrolysis.

How much electricity will be needed to deposit 10 grams of sodium? 96,500 coulombs deposit an equivalent weight of sodium (23 grams). Therefore 10 grams would be deposited by $96,500 \times \frac{10}{23}$ coulombs of electricity. With a fixed current it is quite easy to work out how long the operation will take.

The reverse also holds good. If it is known how much metal has been deposited then it is easy to calculate the quantity of electricity responsible. This is in fact a very accurate way of assessing quantities of electricity. It is usually done by determining the weight of copper deposited on a cathode. Because weighings can be made with great accuracy, the final result is also very accurate. The vessel in which this is performed is known as a *copper voltameter* – an entirely different instrument from a *voltmeter*.

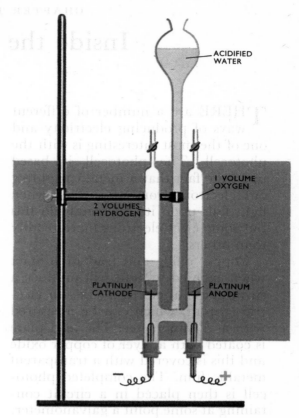

ACIDIFIED WATER

2 VOLUMES HYDROGEN

1 VOLUME OXYGEN

PLATINUM CATHODE

PLATINUM ANODE

Faraday's second law states that *the weights of different substances liberated by the same quantity of electricity are proportional to their chemical equivalents.*

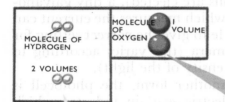

MOLECULE OF HYDROGEN

MOLECULE OF OXYGEN

1 VOLUME

2 VOLUMES

ATOMIC WEIGHT OF — 16 UNITS OXYGEN

WEIGHT OF 1 MOLECULE OF — 32 UNITS OXYGEN

ATOMIC WEIGHT OF — 1 UNIT HYDROGEN

WEIGHT OF — 4 UNITS 2 MOLECULES OF HYDROGEN

4 GM OF HYDROGEN ARE GIVEN OFF FOR EVERY 32 GM OF OXYGEN

THEREFORE FOR EVERY GRAM OF HYDROGEN LIBERATED 8 GMS OF OXYGEN ARE SET FREE.

1 AND 8 ARE THE CHEMICAL EQUIVALENTS OF HYDROGEN AND OXYGEN.

For every gram of hydrogen liberated 8 grams of oxygen are released. 1 and 8 are the chemical equivalents of hydrogen and oxygen. This is in accordance with Faraday's second law of electrolysis.

CHAPTER THIRTY-ONE

Inside the Lightmeter

THERE are a number of different ways of producing electricity and one of the most interesting is with the photocell. The photocell is based upon the fact that a metal can throw out electrons from its surface when light falls upon it. All metals do this but some eject electrons more readily than others.

Copper oxide and lead in contact when exposed to light will produce a strong flow of electrons, i.e. an electric current, which can be measured with a galvanometer. The lead plate is coated with a layer of copper oxide and this is covered with a transparent metallic film. The completed photocell is then placed in a circuit containing at some point a galvanometer. Light passes through the film and strikes the copper oxide, 'knocking' electrons out of it at the surface. These pass to the metallic film where the atoms soon have more than their share of electrons. Now atoms that have less than their share of electrons

attract the electrons of other atoms; since the atoms of the copper oxide are deficient in electrons, they attract electrons from the lead plate. But this process means that atoms of the metallic film become wealthier in electrons than the atoms of the lead plate, so electrons flow from the film, through the *circuit*, to the lead plate to even things up. In other words a small current has been produced.

A photographer's lightmeter contains this kind of photocell (except that selenium usually takes the place of copper oxide because it is more sensitive to light). As the current increases with the intensity of light falling upon the photocell (i.e. more electrons are ejected), a tiny galvanometer which measures the current can be made to give the correct setting for the camera (this varies according to the intensity of the light).

In another form, the photocell is the 'electric eye' in industry which sets off many mechanical processes,

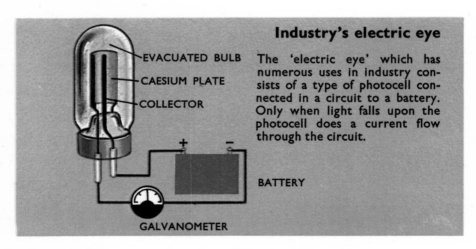

EVACUATED BULB

CAESIUM PLATE

COLLECTOR

+ −

BATTERY

GALVANOMETER

Industry's electric eye

The 'electric eye' which has numerous uses in industry consists of a type of photocell connected in a circuit to a battery. Only when light falls upon the photocell does a current flow through the circuit.

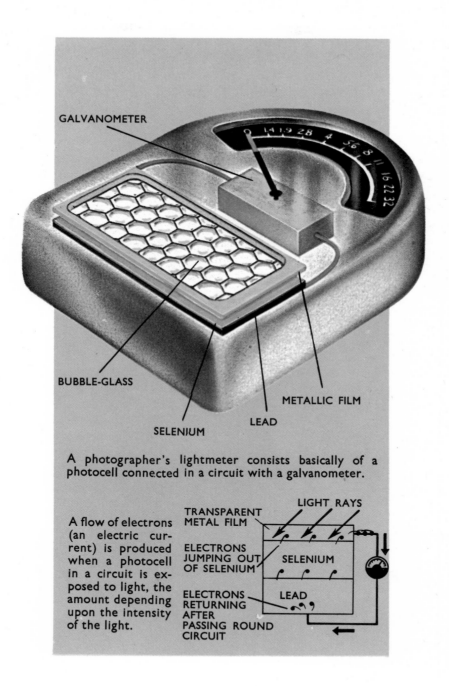

GALVANOMETER

BUBBLE-GLASS

SELENIUM

LEAD

METALLIC FILM

A photographer's lightmeter consists basically of a photocell connected in a circuit with a galvanometer.

A flow of electrons (an electric current) is produced when a photocell in a circuit is exposed to light, the amount depending upon the intensity of the light.

LIGHT RAYS

TRANSPARENT METAL FILM

ELECTRONS JUMPING OUT OF SELENIUM

SELENIUM

ELECTRONS RETURNING AFTER PASSING ROUND CIRCUIT

LEAD

ranging from the wrapping, sorting and weighing of articles to the opening of doors and setting off of burglar alarms. In this case the photocell consists of an evacuated glass tube or bulb containing a plate of one of the light-sensitive metals (often caesium) and a metal rod (not quite touching the plate) called a collector. The photocell is then connected in a circuit to a battery. The principle is much the same as before except that the battery provides the driving force needed to move the ejected electrons across the vacuum. When light falls upon the caesium, electrons are ejected from its surface. They are attracted across to the collector rod because it is kept positively charged by the battery, and is therefore short of electrons. In this way a current only flows when light falls upon the photocell (for when no light reaches the photocell no electrons are ejected from the caesium and there is a break in the circuit between the light-sensitive plate and the collector rod). In a burglar alarm system, for instance, a beam of light (infra-red light so that it cannot be detected by the human eye) shines continuously across a room onto a photocell and keeps a small current flowing. But if anyone interrupts the beam by walking across it the current stops and the alarm is triggered off. In whatever industrial field the photocell is used it depends upon the beam of light falling upon it either varying in intensity or stopping and starting.

CHAPTER THIRTY-TWO

The Thermocouple

THE normal way of producing electricity is either by dynamos, batteries or cells. But there are other ways and one of these, which may be of considerable importance in the future, is based upon the *thermocouple*. This consists simply of two wires of different metals, joined together at both of their ends to form a circuit. As early as 1821 it was found that if any two dissimilar wires are joined together and heat is applied to one junction, a small current is produced, i.e. electrons will flow.

One use of the thermocouple at present is in the *pyrometer*, an instrument for measuring high temperatures, such as those of molten metals. The thermocouple type of pyrometer (there are other types) is based upon the fact that the current increases with the difference in temperature between two junctions. When one junction is heated, in a furnace for instance, the current produced can be measured by a galvanometer placed in the circuit at the cold junction. For high temperatures platinum and platinum-rhodium alloy wires are used. This kind of pyrometer is rarely used above 1,600 degrees centigrade.

One interesting possibility is that the thermocouple might, at some future date, be used to produce electricity direct from atomic energy. At present the heat produced by the break-down of radioactive materials is used to turn water into steam; the steam then drives turbine engines which in turn drive the dynamos which produce the electricity, a long and wasteful process. Experiments have shown that when one junction of a thermocouple is placed in a container of radioactive materials, the heat produced by their break-down immediately produces electricity. A vast number of thermocouples so heated could produce commercial quantities of electricity. The interesting point about this process is that it can use radioactive waste materials

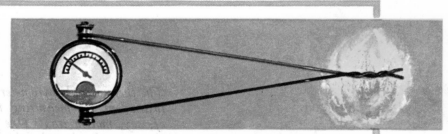

The galvanometer that measures the current produced when one junction of a thermocouple is heated can be made to give the actual temperature once it has been calibrated against objects at known temperatures.

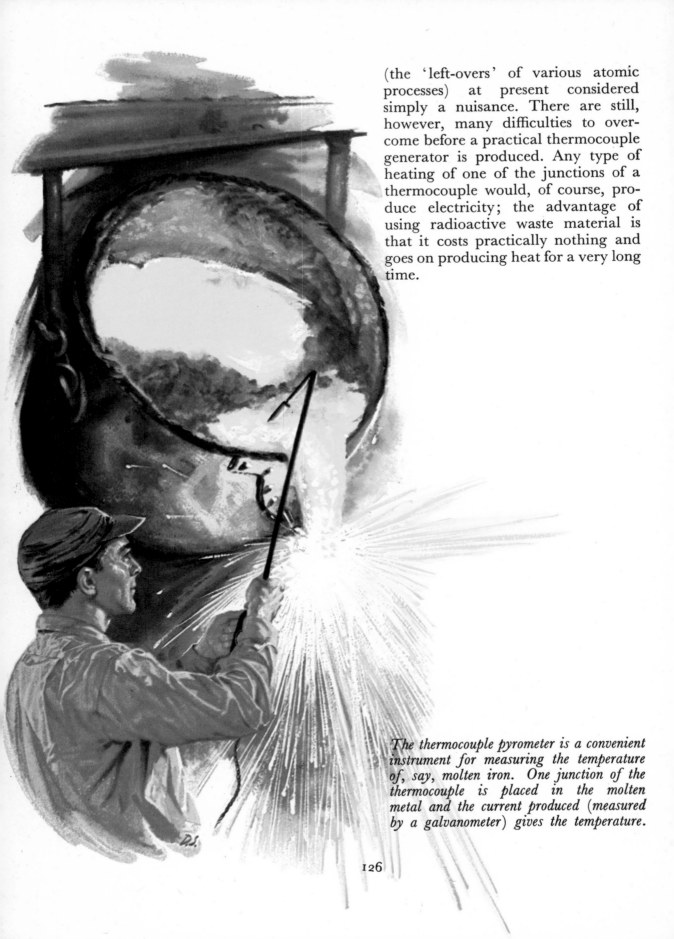

(the 'left-overs' of various atomic processes) at present considered simply a nuisance. There are still, however, many difficulties to overcome before a practical thermocouple generator is produced. Any type of heating of one of the junctions of a thermocouple would, of course, produce electricity; the advantage of using radioactive waste material is that it costs practically nothing and goes on producing heat for a very long time.

The thermocouple pyrometer is a convenient instrument for measuring the temperature of, say, molten iron. One junction of the thermocouple is placed in the molten metal and the current produced (measured by a galvanometer) gives the temperature.

Index

Date Due			
MAR 26 '74			
DEC. 07 1998			
OCT 0 3 2006			
MAR 2 4 2015